ABOUT THE AUTHOR

Alan Wilson gained his doctorate from the University of Manchester with a thesis exploring the history of Manchester's water supply and sanitation. He went on to produce a permanent exhibition on the subject at the Museum of Science and Industry in Manchester, where he was subsequently appointed the curator of the museum's National Electricity Gallery and National Gas Gallery. On moving to Wales, he lectured on the history of technology and civil engineering at Swansea University and with The Open University in Wales.

Throughout his academic career he has researched, written about and lectured on the social and technical history of country houses, and has now brought that research together in this study devoted to the country houses of west Wales.

W0009719

COMFORT, PLEASURE & PRESTIGE

COUNTRY-HOUSE TECHNOLOGY IN WEST WALES 1750-1930

Alan Wilson

Matador
9 Priory Business Park,
Wistow Road, Kibworth Beauchamp,
Leicestershire. LE8 0RX
Tel: 0116 279 2299
Email: books@troubador.co.uk
Web: www.troubador.co.uk/matador
Twitter: @matadorbooks

ISBN 978 1785892 516

British Library Cataloguing in Publication Data.
A catalogue record for this book is available from the British Library.

Printed and bound by CPI Group (UK) Ltd, Croydon, CR0 4YY
Typeset in 11pt Aldine401 BT by Troubador Publishing Ltd, Leicester, UK

Matador is an imprint of Troubador Publishing Ltd

MIX
Paper from
responsible sources
FSC
www.fsc.org   FSC® C013604

To family and friends, past and present.

ACKNOWLEDGEMENTS

I would like to acknowledge the help, support and patience of my wife, Kathryn, without whose help this book would never have come to fruition. I would also like to thank all the many owners, curators, archivists and house stewards of the various houses I visited during my research. It was a tremendous pleasure to meet them, and immensely gratifying and stimulating to see the pride and enthusiasm they demonstrated in their respective houses. Without their willingness to accept my repeated visits and respond to my interminable questions, this book would not have been possible. Notable among those many people who provided help, advice and information are Patrick Mansel Lewis of Stradey Castle, Heddwen Cadwallader of Llanerchaeron, and the staff and volunteers of Newton House. I would also like to thank Louise Davis, my one-time research assistant, for her work on kitchen-garden technology, and Janet Joel for her invaluable help on Nanteos. Finally, I would like to thank Howard Jenkins for his photographic skills, and Leighton Phillips for his work on graphic design. I am also deeply indebted to all the many authors of the secondary sources I have drawn on to support the discussions presented here. Any errors, of course, are entirely my own.

TABLE OF CONTENTS

Map showing locations of houses discussed in the text

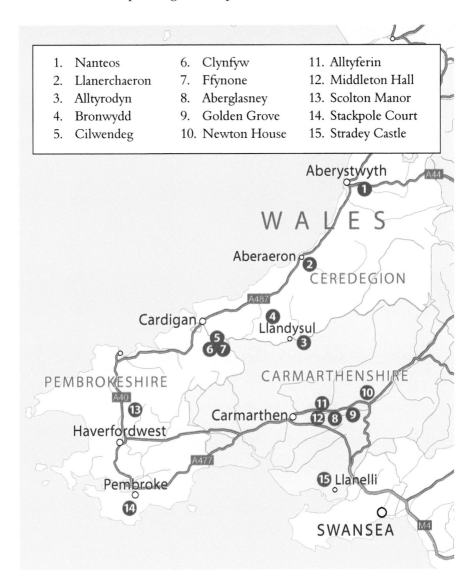

1. Nanteos
2. Llanerchaeron
3. Alltyrodyn
4. Bronwydd
5. Cilwendeg

6. Clynfyw
7. Ffynone
8. Aberglasney
9. Golden Grove
10. Newton House

11. Alltyferin
12. Middleton Hall
13. Scolton Manor
14. Stackpole Court
15. Stradey Castle

Aberystwyth
①

W A L E S

Aberaeron
②

CEREDEGION

A487

Cardigan
⑤
⑥⑦

④
Llandysul
③

PEMBROKESHIRE

A40

⑬

CARMARTHENSHIRE

⑩

Carmarthen
⑪
⑫⑧⑨

Haverfordwest

A477

Pembroke
⑭

⑮ Llanelli

SWANSEA
M4

INTRODUCTION

A great deal has been written about the role of servants in supporting the gentry in their country-house lifestyle, but relatively little on the emerging country-house technologies of the late-nineteenth and early-twentieth centuries. The purpose of this book is to describe the domestic technology used in country houses in west Wales and explain the rationale behind its introduction. Although it is not intended to provide a detailed technical history of individual country houses, a number of them have been drawn on quite extensively to illustrate the ways in which technology was introduced into gentry households more widely. In charting the evolution and development of country-house technology, three broad topic areas have been explored: washing and bathing, water supply and sanitation, and heating and lighting. It is the contention that the gentry only adopted new forms of technology when they saw tangible advantages in doing so. Those advantages included increased comfort and convenience, but domestic technology was rarely adopted simply because it demonstrated some clear technological advance over what had gone before, and certainly not because it eased the servants' burden. While this is not a book devoted to the social or architectural history of country houses, domestic technology can never be entirely divorced from the lives of the people who used it, installed it, and who enjoyed its benefits; while some technologies clearly impacted on the form and fabric of the houses in which they were installed.

For much of the period 1750–1930, the driving force of the Welsh gentry was the pursuit of comfort, pleasure and prestige. Central to achieving their objectives was the country house. It provided a stage on which to entertain, and a showcase in which to display their affluence, status and style. Above all, the country house was a place to enjoy all the comforts and luxuries that wealth and power provided, and to pursue the country sports and recreations that ample leisure time made possible. Although the ability to maintain such a lifestyle was, to a large extent, determined by a family's wealth (or indebtedness), the whole edifice of country-house living was dependant on servants and technology. During the eighteenth and nineteenth centuries, servants using 'traditional' forms of technology were able to provide all the comfort and convenience the Welsh gentry required. However, in the late-nineteenth century, the gentry's expectations of what was deemed to be an appropriate lifestyle rose, along with their aspirations for greater status and prestige. Such rising expectations and aspirations could often only be met by a greater use of modern forms of domestic technology in order to sustain the gentry's comfort, even as their landed incomes declined. This book explores the rise of technology to meet those expectations.

The financial woes of the landed gentry grew increasingly serious in the inter-war period, due to death duties and increased taxation. These economic problems, coupled with a growing inability to recruit and retain domestic servants meant that without modern technology the gentry were no longer able to live in the style to which they had become accustomed. They were faced with a number of options: they could retrench, abandon country-house living altogether, or finally embrace modern technology.

In this book, I will explore the transition from traditional to modern forms of domestic technology in Welsh country houses, against a backdrop of the changing relationship between the gentry's passion for pleasure and prestige, the availability of servants, and the emerging technologies of the nineteenth and twentieth centuries. In 1750, country houses were heated by open fires and lit by candles; chamber pots were almost the only means of sanitation; and the gentry washed and bathed in their bedrooms, using portable hip baths and washbowls. By 1930, virtually all Welsh country houses had electric lighting, central heating, flush toilets, and hot and cold running water. Impressive though those changes might appear, the Welsh gentry were rarely in the van of technological innovation during that period and many of those advances were often only slowly, almost reluctantly, introduced into Welsh country houses.

In tandem with advances in domestic technology, there was also rapid growth in the range and availability of domestic appliances, particularly electrical appliances. Again, until after the Second World War, few such appliances found their way into Welsh country houses, and most landowners appear to have been remarkably reluctant to adopt new technologies and appliances. That reluctance has generally been attributed to the availability of servants to undertake the multitude of household tasks, chores and duties necessary to keep a gentry household running smoothly. However, it is not the only reason. Other factors also came into play, including the desire to retain traditional standards, the financial and logistical problems involved in introducing new technology in remote country areas, and the prestige and convenience of having servants constantly at one's beck and call. With regard to electrical appliances, of course, that was ultimately dependent on whether or not there was an electrical supply capable of running them.

Paradoxically, although the Welsh gentry were somewhat reluctant to invest in basic technologies such as central heating and indoor plumbing, other forms of technology were eagerly seized upon, logistical problems were overcome, and large-scale expenditure undertaken. The choice of which technologies were adopted reveals a great deal about the primary motivations of the Welsh gentry. As Baker-Jones notes, 'Lacking a sense of priorities, they preferred to spend vast sums on new mansions, on expensive lifestyles and unbridled "display"' (1999, p.104). In adopting such a hedonistic lifestyle, basic advances in domestic technology were often largely ignored.

With ample servants to tend fires, clean and empty chamber pots, and carry water for washing and bathing, there was little incentive to invest in central heating, flush toilets, and hot and cold running water. Such technologies did little to enhance the gentry's comfort, convenience or status. Conversely, electric lighting, ornamental fountains, the ability to grow rare and exotic fruit, and to enjoy chilled drinks in summer, achieved all of those aims. In short, the Welsh gentry used a combination of servants and technology to enjoy a high level of luxury and convenience – whatever the time of day, or the season of the year. At the same time, they used their servants and some very specific forms of technology to demonstrate their wealth and status.

In fairness, the inadequacies of some forms of technology also played a part in their slow take-up in country houses. Early central heating systems were notoriously inefficient, gas lighting was dirty and smelly, and water closets often malfunctioned and were widely seen as potential health hazards.

Contemporary accounts and descriptions of country-house technology rarely appear in letters, diaries or journals, and, as a consequence, first-hand accounts of its installation and day-to-day use are strictly limited. The topic was seen either as a taboo subject – too private and personal to be discussed in polite society – or too mundane to be of note. The problem of there being such limited discussion of domestic technology has, however, been largely overcome in this book by its study of architects' plans, inventories and contemporary sales literature, as well as by undertaking numerous site visits. Such varied sources, augmented by anecdotal evidence, have allowed a light – admittedly, a flickering one – to be shone into some of the more hidden recesses of country-house living in the eighteenth, nineteenth and early-twentieth centuries. The one thing that is abundantly clear from the research is that country-house technology was installed primarily for the benefit of the gentry, and not for the ease or convenience of domestic servants. As Jill Franklin points out, 'Country house owners would install new appliances only if they were convinced…that their comfort would be increased by doing so' (Franklin, 1991, p.107).

This book explores the gentry's changing and evolving relationship with technology to meet their continuing desire for comfort, pleasure and prestige.

Society and Change

In the eighteenth and nineteenth centuries, the urban elite, by making use of emerging technologies delivered by private enterprise or municipal initiative could gain relatively easy access to services such as water supply, sanitation, and ultimately mains drainage, gas and electricity. The landed gentry, on the other hand, living far from centres of population, had to rely on their servants and whatever technology they could provide for themselves to meet their day-to-day needs.

The gentry's enforced reliance on servants and traditional technology still allowed them to live in comfort, luxury and ease, and had the additional benefit of raising their prestige in the eyes of their peers, as well as providing employment in the local community. With such an abundance of servants to draw on, there was little incentive for the Welsh squirearchy to invest in technologies that would largely be hidden from view, and would not significantly increase their comfort, pleasure or prestige. In short, so long as they were happy with the status quo, they saw no reason to change their old established ways. Mrs John Farrar, describing the Welsh gentry at the close of the eighteenth century, wrote:

> The descendants of the most ancient families prided themselves on adhering to the old customs of the country, and disdained the idea of importing London fashions and manners…The roads were ill made and never kept in repair, and this made riding on horseback a favourite mode of conveyance. I have been one of a large dinner-party, to which every guest went on horseback, and all the ladies dined in their cloth habits and rode home many miles at night… (Farrar, 1865, pp.41-2).

Similarly, Fenton, describing the Morgan family of Blaenbylan, Pembrokeshire in 1810, wrote that though the Morgan family's:

…possessions in this county were very extensive, well wooded, contiguous, and finely circumstanced in every respect. The house situated in the most objectionable part of the demesne, was meanly and irregularly built as to its exterior, and within consisted of several small, low, and dismally dark rooms, the whole quite disproportionate to the fortune and the rank of the former inhabitants…a circumstance I find it difficult to account for in any other way than by supposing that, generation after generation, they continued to reside at home among their vassals and tenants, and had never suffered ambition to wean them from that primitive mode of life, by inviting them to mix with the world, and affect more elegant habits, and contract a taste for expensive innovation (Fenton, 1810, p.146).

For much of the eighteenth and nineteenth centuries, the Welsh gentry remained firmly entrenched in their traditional ways of conducting their lives and households. They took pride in established patterns of behaviour, of routine and in running their affairs in time-honoured ways.

Such an approach might be seen as primarily reflecting the views of 'old money' the quintessentially, long-established landed interests, but that was not entirely the case. When the *nouveaux riches* urban merchants, bankers and industrialists bought country houses, they firmly embraced traditional styles of living and traditional ways of running their households – rather than installing the latest technology. That adoption of what may appear to have been almost archaic behaviour is not surprising; such arriviste families bought country houses to enjoy the pleasures, privileges and political power of the landed elite, and therefore consciously sought to assimilate the values and trappings of the country squire. As Taine wrote in the 1880s:

…nearly all the men, who by their talent or by their industry have grown wealthy, have an ambition to acquire an estate, to fix their family on it, and to enter the local aristocracy (Taine, 1885, p.166).

To be fully accepted, they emulated and adopted the lifestyle of the local squirearchy:

Entry into the social circle of the landed gentry, the prime object of the new men who laid out their savings in land purchase, was achieved with ease provided that the newcomer adopted the conventions of gentry behaviour in his style of living and pursuit of country interests (Thompson, 1963, p.127).

Often those who are new to wealth and gentility will be the most punctilious in keeping up standards, partly because they wish to endorse a world they have worked so hard to enter, and partly because they are afraid of making mistakes or showing that they do not 'know the form' (Paterson, 2012, p.9).

Mark Girouard, describing that process of assimilation, stated:

…on the whole the new arrivals did none of the things that *nouveaux riches* are supposed to do. They were neither aggressive, inept nor ostentatious. They subscribed to local charities, sent their sons to the right schools and hunted, shot and fished with enthusiasm, if not always with skill. They were eager to be accepted (Giouard, 1984, p.268).

It would though be an oversimplification to divide country-house owners neatly into two groups: the old-established families and the *nouveaux riches*. Many of the Welsh landed gentry had interests in mining and industry, and many younger sons of landed families entered commerce and the professions. Then, having made their fortunes, they returned to the land and welcomed the opportunity to resume the style of living they had grown accustomed to in their youth.

A reluctance to embrace technology was not based solely on a desire to cling tenaciously to traditional ways of running a household. Decisions about installing new technology were also strongly influenced by the varying fortunes of individual families. The finances of the landed gentry – or, at least, those not blessed with significant external sources of income – often fluctuated erratically and precariously. Levels of indebtedness, opportune or inopportune marriages, rising and falling income from agriculture and farm rentals – to say nothing of personal predilections leading to excessive drinking or gambling – all influenced the financial stability of gentry-households. Describing the eighteenth-century gentry of south-west

Wales, David Howell writes:

> Too much was spent by all categories of the gentry within the
> region on acquiring new lands…meeting gambling debts, financing
> election contests, personal extravagance, legal disputes, children's
> education and capital sums for younger members of the family
> (Howell, 1986, p. 216).

With those dangers in mind, many landowners placed legal restrictions
(entails) on what could or could not be sold or mortgaged in an attempt
to restrict the ability of their heirs to reduce the size and value of the
estate:

> The needs of status and family implied continuing control over
> the estate to see that its revenues were not eroded by extravagance
> or irresponsibility. Under the care of a prudent heir all might be
> well, but not all heirs were prudent. Clearly it was essential in the
> interests of the family at large to establish means of securing the
> inheritance from the depredations of the heir who turned out an
> unrestrained builder, a rash speculator, inveterate gambler, over–
> ambitious politician, or mere incompetent (Mingay, 1976, p.109).

Even allowing for restrictions on how money could be raised, and given
all the various ways that an inheritance could be squandered, the Welsh
gentry were still generally in a position to introduce new forms of domestic
technology into their homes – if they wished to do so. Such technology
was almost always included when new houses were being built or when
major renovation work was being undertaken, while small, piece-meal
installations such as a water closet could easily be provided on a more ad
hoc basis. In spite of all the legal constraints, rebuilding and extending
country houses was surprisingly commonplace in both the eighteenth and
nineteenth centuries.

The almost obsessive desire to aggrandise or even entirely relocate
country houses in the eighteenth and nineteenth centuries was
driven both by changing fashions in country-house architecture and
a growing desire for more picturesque settings. The gentry, especially
those rising up the social scale, believed it to be their innate right to
live in ease and opulence. Accordingly, they built, rebuilt, enlarged and

refurbished their homes to reflect their real (or, sometimes, imagined) status. To achieve their objectives, existing properties were totally refashioned, even relocated, to make them appear more impressive from afar or to provide better views over rolling parkland. Inevitably, in the process, some families over-extended themselves and there are many examples of excessive 'home-improvement' leading to dangerous levels of indebtedness. Peterwell and Bronwydd are, perhaps, the two most obvious examples in the region of extravagant over-expenditure (Phillips, 1997; Baker-Jones, 2005).

Unfortunately, the gentry's compelling urge to enlarge and enhance their homes meant that many country houses became unsustainable when economic decline struck in the late-nineteenth century, and when servants became harder to recruit in the twentieth. Houses that had originally been quite modest gentry houses – albeit with a substantial kitchen, and one or two bedrooms for servants – became impracticable as homes for twentieth-century families after being enlarged and provided with extensive service ranges. Furthermore, if land and other assets had been sold off to fund ambitious building schemes, when the inevitable agricultural depression struck, the income from the estate was even less able to sustain a country-house lifestyle.

Even by the late-nineteenth century, when governmental fiscal policy and various Reform Acts were making it increasingly obvious that land-ownership was no longer the key to power, wealth and prestige, many gentry families could still not face that grim reality. They clung tenaciously to the belief that their elite position in society would be maintained and that the old order would somehow be restored. They saw it, therefore, as their duty to ensure that their descendants would inherit an elegant and prestigious country house. If they chose to build conservatories or billiard rooms, they did so – even if it incurred additional debt. Furthermore, the Welsh gentry of the eighteenth and nineteenth centuries were not widely renowned for deferred gratification. It was really only during the inter-war period that they began to seriously attempt to live within their means and to fully embrace the benefits of domestic technology – particularly central heating, indoor plumbing and electric lighting.

That new awareness was largely a result of the onset of the First World War, when a lack of domestic servants prompted the introduction of rudimentary forms of modern technology. Even before conscription was introduced, country-house owners had been exhorted to encourage their male servants to enlist and their female servants to take up war work. Many domestic servants answered the call, and when large-scale conscription was finally introduced, the exodus from domestic service accelerated still further. Many male servants never returned from the front, and the majority of those who did had little desire to re-enter domestic service. Furthermore, after the war far fewer young men and women were willing to accept the servility, petty regulations and restrictions that went with domestic service. It was no longer seen as a secure and appealing long-term career. Working-class men and women could experience greater freedom, earn more, enjoy better marriage prospects and have more self-esteem working in factories, shops and offices, than by being 'in service'. The servant problem, though a perennial one, grew dramatically in scale after the First World War.

Not only were fewer young men and women willing to enter service, but the wages and demands of those who did were significantly higher than before the War. Unfortunately, for the gentry, that shift took place at precisely the time that their own incomes were being squeezed still further:

> Economic and social factors, spurred on by the 1914–18 war, meant a shortage of cheap labour and cheap fuel. Increased taxes on income and transferred property made a large country house no longer a viable asset. Many estates were heavily mortgaged…and landowners had eventually to abandon the homes their families had lived in for centuries (Baker-Jones, 1999, p.144).

In the inter-war period, the landed gentry were hit by a cruel combination of increased indebtedness, taxation, death duties and falling estate revenue. Estate duty on estates worth more than £2 million, for example, went up to 40 per cent in 1919 (though that probably didn't affect many estates in west Wales). By the 1920s, rates and taxes were taking about 30 per cent of an estate's rental income (Paterson, 2012, p.259).

The days of lavish entertaining became a thing of the past, and that trend impacted particularly heavily on the Welsh gentry whose estates tended to be smaller and less productive than their English counterparts. Small estates suffered disproportionately when agriculture went into decline and many country houses were sold off, to be bought by families not entirely reliant on an income from the land to fund a country-house lifestyle. Such families could more easily afford to install the latest technology in their newly acquired homes, and changing fashions in the 1920s encouraged them to do so.

Yet, against all the odds, and in the face of rising costs and diminishing income, some gentry families still clung resolutely to their country houses, struggling on in ever more faded gentility. In the process, they were often forced by circumstances to install some basic forms of domestic technology, simply to make survival without servants a realistic possibility. As a result of these converging factors, by 1930 most country houses in Wales had electric lighting, hot and cold running water, flush toilets and at least partial central heating. In some cases, that was as a result of rising expectations and aspirations, but in others it was simply a matter of necessity and expediency. As long as there had been a pool of readily available domestic servants to cook and clean, and to fetch and carry, there was little incentive to invest in new technology. When changing circumstances led to those duties being carried out less often, less diligently and less adequately, either by a diminishing number of servants or, even more gallingly, by members of the family themselves, there was a growing imperative to introduce new technology and new labour-saving devices.

Hedonism, Hospitality
and Status

'We frequently found the most retired alehouses filled with the middling gentry, who count it unbecoming to retire sober' (quoted in Howell, 1986, p.221).

That comment – made by Henry Wyndham in 1774 while travelling through west Wales – eloquently sums up the gentry's devotion to hard drinking in the eighteenth century. While other groups in society may have been equally fond of strong liquor, the gentry had the advantage of having more time and money to indulge in the pastime. The quote also highlights the fact that small gentry estates in the region were in such close proximity that filling alehouses with the sons of the local squirearchy was relatively easy to achieve.

Although the Georgian gentry may have been renowned more for their hard drinking and love of country sports than their social refinement, that Squire Western-like image changed dramatically in the nineteenth century. In the nineteenth century, the gentry became noticeably more involved in religion, local charities, culture and the arts – but, even then, pleasure-seeking and the need to maintain or enhance their social status still strongly influenced their behaviour. Although country sports continued to dominate the pursuit of pleasure, other – arguably, more innocuous – forms of recreation began to emerge. However, status was still generally achieved by living in prestigious country houses, by lifestyle, and by public service as Justices of the Peace, High Sheriffs, Lord Lieutenants and Members of Parliament.

The gentry sought to impress. Naturally, therefore, they chose to spend their money embellishing their homes with fine furniture and furnishings, rather than on labour-saving devices for their servants. That willingness to spend lavishly in the pursuit of pleasure and prestige clearly influenced the gentry's decision-making. For the Welsh gentry, the key factors determining any form of expenditure were the amount of comfort and pleasure it provided, how much it demonstrated the family's wealth and hospitality, and how far it went in supporting and enhancing the family's position in society.

Mrs Farrar, writing in1865, stated that the Welsh gentry:

> …are very proud of their pedigrees, tracing back their ancestry far beyond the Norman Conquest. Many of them have lost much of their ancestral possessions, but none of their pride, and make great efforts to keep up a grand appearance on small means (Farrar, 1865, p.40).

The eighteenth and nineteenth centuries saw significant changes in farming practice, industry, transport and political power, but for the Welsh gentry, the pursuit of comfort, pleasure and prestige remained paramount. The emphasis may have shifted slightly from hard drinking, gambling and country sports, to billiards, croquet and archery, but in one form or other, gentry families remained fixated on pleasure. Although the head of the family may have been required to devote much of his time to estate management, business and politics, junior members of the family needed alternative diversions to fill their days. In some instances, the time on their hands was channelled into charitable or religious work, but more often it was devoted to games, socialising, reading, painting and embroidery. Along with house parties, balls and excursions, such hobbies and pastimes helped prevent insufferable boredom and provided the social glue that bonded members of the local elite together. The pursuit of pleasure, therefore, helps to explain why the gentry invested so much time, money and effort into recreational facilities, rather than on mundane forms of domestic technology.

Recreation took many forms; while foxhunting, hare coursing and otter hunting remained popular – with packs of hounds being kept at Nanteos, Ffynone, Bronwydd, etc. – shooting and fishing were also widely followed.

Fig 1. Spence Colby (on the left), of Ffynone, with his foxhounds.

The Welsh gentry not only revelled in the hunt but saw it as a means of asserting their position in society and of raising their status. Henry Williams Howell (1801-1880) of Glaspant, for example, was seen as:

> …a typical jolly and jovial sporting squire: Master of the 'Tivy-side' foxhounds, jointly with Capt. Lewes-Lloyd from 1826-31. He was very proud of his stud of tip-top hunters, the breeding of which was the old gentleman's chief delight (Baker-Jones, 2001, p.11).

Similarly, William Powell ran the Nanteos estate primarily for pheasant shooting, and otter and fox hunting (Palmer, et al, 2004, p.69). And when Sir Marteine Lloyd inherited the Bronwydd estate in 1877 (along with debts of £94,000), he was seen as:

> …the epitome of the sporting squire: hunting, fishing, breeding fine horses, supporting the United Counties Hunters' Society, the Carmarthenshire Hunt Steeplechase, and proud owner of the Bronwydd Beagles and the Bronwydd Hounds (Baker-Jones, 2005, p.135).

Sir Marteine was nothing if not a flamboyant sportsman; for example, when out hunting, he carried a whip with an 'ebony handle, studded with pearls & very handsome' (Baker-Jones, 2001, p.148). Even by contemporary standards, Sir Marteine Lloyd was perhaps excessively devoted to country sports, but David Lewis of Stradey , who may be seen as a more representative example of the Welsh squirearchy, was also a keen country sportsman, as his diary entries for a typical week in 1822 show:

- *Monday, 12 August* – Went out shooting with John Price killed one grouse had two long shots
- *Tuesday, 13 August* – Went a second time over the hills had one very long shot
- *Wednesday, 14 August* – Rained all day
- *Thursday, 15 August* – Went on the hills, no sport…dined at Glangwily
- *Friday, 16 August* – Walked to Pant-yr-Sait with the dogs
- *Saturday, 17 August* – Went on the hills no sport…Mr & Mrs Lloyd Laques [Laques mansion, Llanstephan] came to Glangwily
- *Sunday, 18 August* – Went to church

At the time, he was in his mid-twenties. However, twenty-five years later, by which time he was the High Sheriff of Carmarthen and had served as a Member of Parliament, his diary entries were much the same. Although they included references to public duties, committee and business meetings, etc., they still focused primarily on where he had walked and ridden, what he had shot and with whom he had dined. He lived an active outdoor life, until he died suddenly and unexpectedly at his London club in 1872, aged seventy-five.

Although hunting, shooting and fishing remained popular outdoor pursuits throughout the period 1750–1930, tennis and croquet grew in popularity in the nineteenth century. Indeed, by the end of that century, most country houses boasted tennis courts and croquet lawns. Billiards also became popular in

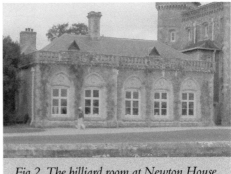

Fig 2. The billiard room at Newton House.

the nineteenth century, with many country houses adding a billiard room to their ground plan – as at Newton House, Stradey Castle, Nanteos and Cilwendeg.

Fig 3. The billiard room at Llanerchaeron built in 1843 by John Lewis, the somewhat rakish owner of the house. It was virtually the only addition or improvement he made to the house during his tenure (Palmer, et al, 2004, p.58).

Billiards was predominantly a male recreation, and the billiard room primarily a male preserve. It was where business and politics were discussed. It was also where heavy drinking and smoking could be enjoyed, away from the disapproving gaze of the ladies. Smoking was seen as being particularly distasteful due to the tobacco fumes it generated. As a consequence, smokers were often banished outdoors, or to billiard or smoking rooms where the ventilation of such rooms could be given special attention by the architects. Kerr, for example, wrote in 1864:

> …care must be taken to shut it [the billiard room] off not only from the Public-rooms but even the chief Thoroughfares; and it ought to be so ventilated that the passage of the smoke from the windows may not be a nuisance in any way (Kerr, 1864, p.134).

Although billiards and cards were the most popular indoor pursuits, and foxhunting remained the most popular outdoor sport, there was a wide range of other indoor and outdoor activities available to amuse the gentry. The journal of Hermione Jennings of Gellideg, written in the 1860s, is full of entries describing her leisure interests. At the time she was writing, she was in her late teens and her interests included archery, croquet, dances, balls, playing charades and coracling. Coracling might appear to be an unusual pursuit for a genteel, young Victorian lady, especially considering the fashionably heavy clothing she would have been wearing, but it was a

Fig 4. Coracling at Dirleton.

surprisingly popular form of recreation among the Welsh gentry.
Her diary entries vividly describe many of the pastimes she indulged in:

> Thursday. Showery. Went about the grounds with Miss Gulston,
> Mamma, and Richie. Then we went in the boat on the river, and I
> went a little way in the coracle with Stepney Gulston…I went into
> dinner with Mr Jones of Velindre…After dinner there was a dance
> in the dining room which was kept up till 1.
>
> Friday. Very showery. I played croquet on the new ground with
> Lizzie Gulston and her brothers and Harry…It came on to rain
> several times very hard but we went on playing all the same with
> cloaks and umbrellas.
>
> On Thursday the 7th of August…We played croquet all the
> afternoon on the lawn. There were three sets, and people came
> dropping in all the afternoon…At 7 we left off playing and got ready
> for dinner…We all wore high white muslin dresses and wore natural
> flowers in our hair. We had dinner at about a quarter to eight…After
> dinner we had dancing in the hall…but we were obliged to dance
> round the billiard table which was too heavy to be moved (Jennings
> Journal, *The Carmarthenshire Historian*, Vol. XI, pp.46-7).

The pastimes indulged in by Hermione were those of a high-spirited,
healthy young woman. For the elderly and infirm, and those suffering
debility caused by decades of heavy drinking and over indulgence, repairing
the ravages of time was attended to by more passive forms of recreation,
such as taking the waters at Bath or Llandrindod Wells.

While the main attractions of Bath were probably more social than
therapeutic, taking the waters did spark an interest amongst the gentry in
hydrotherapy and drinking water from mineral springs. That interest led to
the use of cold-water plunge baths in the grounds of a number of country
houses. Although there are few surviving examples of plunge baths in west
Wales, there is an extremely attractive one (though now sadly derelict) at
Alltyrodyn. Built in the 1790s, in woodland a short distance from the house,
it consisted of two rooms, one enclosing the plunge bath (several feet deep,
but just a few feet square), while the other was used as a changing room. A
leat (an open water channel) fed spring water into the bath and another leat
carried the outflow away to a dipping pond in the nearby walled garden.

Fig 5. The plunge bath at Alltyrodyn.

At about the same time that the bath house at Alltyrodyn was being built, Sir William Paxton was building an even more sophisticated one in the grounds of Middleton Hall. It was built over a mineral spring and had a dressing room, complete with a stove to heat the water and keep the bathers warm while they changed. An indoor plunge bath has also recently been uncovered on the ground floor of Cilwendeg Mansion. It probably dates back to the early-nineteenth century, but by 1906 it had been boarded over and abandoned. It is broadly similar in design and construction to those recommended by Kerr in 1864:

> An ordinary Plunge-bath will be 5 or 6 feet square, and of depth not to exceed 5 feet; with a platform on one side about 4 feet wide...
> It may be placed at any convenient spot in connexion with the Ground-Floor of the Main House...(Kerr, 1864, p.169).

Plunge baths were intended to create an enjoyable, invigorating experience; they may have been believed to be therapeutic, but had little to do with personal cleanliness.

Over time, the excessive self-indulgence, drunkenness and decadence of the eighteenth century declined, and by the end of the nineteenth century, the Welsh gentry were generally well-educated, sophisticated, upright members of society. They gave to charity, endowed schools, funded churches, and improved their estates. Some were even heavily involved in art and literature. Charles Mansel Lewis of Stradey Castle, for example, was a talented artist and keen supporter of the arts; George Powell of Nanteos immersed himself in art and literature, and revelled in the company of London-based artists and poets such as Swinburne. Sir Thomas Lloyd of Bronwydd was a member of the Cambrian Archaeological Association, the Newcastle Emlyn Literary Society, and helped establish the Newport Eisteddfod. Extensive private libraries were also established in country houses across west Wales, notably at Alltyrodyn and Picton Castle. That is not, however, to characterise the Welsh gentry as an elite group of scholarly aesthetes, 'Intellectual and artistic interests were acceptable but not essential' (Girouard, 1984, p.271).

Though priorities may have shifted somewhat during the Victorian and Edwardian periods, the Welsh gentry remained firmly wedded to their country sports. Indeed, even when incomes were squeezed, they continued to keep their packs of hounds and fund their local hunts. They also carried on embellishing their country houses and lived as lavishly as funds allowed. Given that their overall comfort was already taken care of by their servants and traditional forms of domestic technology, it is hardly surprising that pleasure-seeking and status took priority over indoor plumbing and central heating.

That apparent lack of interest in advances in domestic technology was largely due to the lifestyle enjoyed by country landowners. In the Georgian period, and for much of the nineteenth century, the typical Welsh squire would wake to the sound of a maid lighting a fire in his dressing room. He would make his way there to find hot water for washing and shaving waiting for him, and his towel and day clothes warming in front of a fire. After washing and dressing, he would go downstairs to enjoy a hearty breakfast in a room already warmed by another fire. While at breakfast, a housemaid would go to his bedroom to empty and clean his chamber pot and washbowl, make his bed and air his bedroom. Given such a pleasurable start to the day, it is hardly surprising that he felt disinclined to install a central-heating system capable of only taking the chill off the air, of using a water closet that might allow dangerous sewer gas to enter his bedroom, or to wash in tepid water, piped noisily and laboriously from a boiler far away in the bowels of the service range.

While those contrasting pictures are a little overdrawn, they do help to explain why some forms of technology were not more widely adopted and why some families chose instead to spend their money landscaping their parkland, or on fine paintings and furnishings. Such expenditure provided tangible symbols of wealth, taste, sophistication and status; investing in indoor plumbing did not. Comfort and convenience, though almost entirely reliant on a servant-based system, was already largely taken for granted:

> The country house way of life could not exist without servants… landowners hired servants to relieve themselves of what they saw as the demeaning, defiling, menial tasks of cooking, housework, laundry, childcare, stablework, and gardening…they utilized servants as status symbols and actors in ceremonial social rituals… the country house required constant, labour-intensive maintenance. The laborious methods of heating, lighting, and bathing made these tasks more arduous in the country house, as servants had to carry coals, water, and slops much further and more often, clean more steel-grated fireplaces, and light and clean more lamps. Even when gas, piped water and, later, electricity, became available, many landowners stubbornly resisted the new technology as untraditional and decadent (Gerard, 1994, p.142).

While much of the work of servants was largely hidden from view, there was still prestige to be gained from having servants in constant attendance:

> …well-to-do families employed as large a staff as they could afford, since by so doing they could impress the world with the grandeur of their style of living and could indicate that they were persons of consequence (Horn, 1990, p.18).

Not all servants fulfilled that requirement, however. While butlers and footmen clearly did, the bulk of indoor servants were required to be almost invisible – hidden from sight in the service range, or scurrying up and

21

down the backstairs and along service corridors. Even so, the advantages of having numerous servants to supply one's every need was hard to match using the emerging technologies of much of the eighteenth and nineteenth centuries. Many landowners therefore resisted change, preferring instead to run their homes in time-honoured and traditional fashion, while still ensuring that their day-to-day needs were fully met, and their comfort and convenience guaranteed.

Hospitality was, of course, a key feature of the country-house lifestyle. Living long distances from major towns and cities, the Welsh gentry were left to their own devices in terms of providing pleasure and recreation. Entertaining and being entertained therefore featured prominently in the social milieu. Although assembly rooms for polite society grew in popularity during the nineteenth century – for example, those in Aberystwyth were built in 1820, and those at Carmarthen in 1854 – the country house remained the focal point for most forms of entertainment among the squirearchy.

Hermione Jennings regularly described the visits she made to country houses in the region, and the type of recreation provided there. There would typically be a formal dinner, followed by a dance or amateur theatricals, card playing and charades. During the day, there would be hunting, shooting, archery or croquet. Given the poor state of the roads, and the distances needing to be travelled, it was quite common for young ladies to stay overnight when attending a dinner or ball. Doing so enabled them to dress in their finery and, helped by their maids, attend to their hair and make-up in the comfort and privacy of their own rooms. As dances and balls tended to continue well into the early hours of the morning, providing overnight accommodation for a large number of guests was therefore also an essential part of hosting such events. This meant numerous guest bedrooms had to be provided in any country house with pretentions of grandeur. Furthermore, for the sake of decorum, separate guest corridors needed to be provided for male and female visitors.

Hermione Jennings' journal gives a flavour of the sort of hospitality provided. On a visit to Stradey Castle in 1867 she wrote:

Thursday the 10th of January, Mamma and I, with Wakerford and Lewis [servants] went to dine and sleep at Stradey. Papa rode over…Found Mr and Mrs Lewis and young Lewis and Papa in the drawing room. Had tea and then went to dress. I had a good big room…Mr Onslow, Mr Somerset, and Mr Pemberton dined there. I went in to dinner with Mr Onslow. I sang a little in the evening but not well as I had a sore throat…

Breakfast the next day at 10. We left at 12. The meet of Mr Lewis's beagles at Killymanllwd…saw the hounds throw off, then walked back to the carriage (Jennings Journal, *The Carmarthenshire Historian*, Vol. XII, p.22).

On a visit to Pantglas to attend a ball at Aberglasney, she wrote:

On Wednesday the 23rd of January, mamma and I went to stay for three days with the Jones' of Pantglas…In the Hall we met Mr Jones and then the Miss Jones and the youngest boy little Girwin Jones who was about 10, a good-looking child with large prominent teeth…After tea we were taken to our room, we were to have the same…The room was rather cold and cheerless, the window was just being shut as we came in and the fire only just lighted. There was only one washing-stand and one basin…I went in to dinner with Stepney Gulston, after which we dressed for the Aberglasney Ball.

We went in the carriage with Horatia and George Gulston, and Alfred and Louise Jones, so we were tightly packed. We drove round to the back entrance at Aberglasney as they danced in the hall. There were about 100 people…We left at 5. I came back with Stepney, George, and Mr Gulston, Lilla and Louise Jones: they had another supper when they returned but I went off to bed

Friday, Fine day. Came down to breakfast about 11.30…helped to prepare the drawing room for the ball…I went in to dinner with Mr Somerset, and George Gulston was on my other side. Directly after dinner we went to dress…We had a capital ball, about 80 people came. I danced a good deal…After the cotillion [a dance from France] there was a second edition of supper, after which we set to work to dance again which we kept up till 6 but which was at last stopped by the band playing "God Save the Queen" (Jennings Journal, *The Carmarthenshire Historian*, Vol. XII, pp.23; 24; 26-7).

Even an occasional influx of guests put a strain on a household, not only in terms of the food and refreshments needing to be prepared and served, but also in terms of providing washing and bathing facilities. Of course, water for washing and bathing was of secondary importance when compared to wine and beer provision. Vast amounts of alcohol were consumed when entertaining, and an extensive range of fine wines was seen as the mark of a true gentleman. The wine cellars of Sir Herbert Lloyd of Peterwell, for example, were widely renowned for their contents, and he even had his wine bottles personalised with his name and the date of each vintage (Phillips, 1983, p.165). Although wine was not produced on Welsh country estates, beer certainly was, and brewing beer was an important element of country-house technology for much of the eighteenth and nineteenth centuries.

Status was, therefore, achieved by a combination of hospitality, a lavish lifestyle and demonstrations of opulence, breeding and political power. That drive for status was a feature of both the eighteenth and nineteenth centuries, and was not always restrained by lack of funds. Throughout his life, Sir Herbert Lloyd of Peterwell strove for power, titles, and prestige, despite the fact that he was almost constantly in debt:

> ...the passion for elegance and the mania to show style in all things drove the country squires into often crippling competitive extravagance. Money or no money, Sir Herbert was not going to suffer Peterwell to lag behind in its manifestation of grandeur... his envy was stirred by Nanteos which, recently completed after some twenty years of rebuilding, now represented one of the finest examples of Georgian architecture in the whole of west Wales (Phillips, 1997, p.147).

Hedonism, hospitality and status came together in the country house. They overlapped and intertwined. The country house was much more than a place to simply live in; it was where local rivalries could be played out, where political ambitions could be nurtured and developed, where rank and status could be promoted and displayed, and where personal idiosyncrasies and predilections could be enjoyed, often unhindered by social mores and conventions.

Service Range Technology

Although largely hidden from the view of family, guests and visitors, the most important suite of rooms in any country house was its service range. Throughout the eighteenth and nineteenth centuries, the service range remained pivotal in providing the landed gentry with the levels of comfort, luxury and convenience they sought. Not only was food for the family and their guests prepared and cooked in the service range, but it was where soiled linen was washed and ironed, where beer was brewed, where milk was processed into butter, cream and cheese, and from where the hot and cold water for washing and bathing was delivered to the various bedrooms.

The basic techniques involved in cooking, laundering, brewing, dairying, etc., go back many centuries, and while during the eighteenth and nineteenth centuries, a number of significant technical advances were introduced in some areas – notably the kitchen – other service-range activities remained virtually unchanged. In the twentieth century, however, many of the tasks traditionally performed in the service range were abandoned, and instead were undertaken by commercial suppliers and manufacturers. This chapter explores the development and evolution of service-range technology, and the rationale behind the ultimate abandonment of many service-range activities.

Although in its heyday, the bulk of the work carried out in the service range was labour intensive, it was also generally the focal point for any new technology introduced into country houses. But before discussing the technologies involved, it is worth describing briefly the spatial relationship between the typical country house and its service range. Country houses were designed and built on the assumption that there would always be ample servants to provide for all the family's creature comforts. An indication of the importance of the service range in achieving its aims is the fact that almost as much space was devoted to the 'offices' and servants' accommodation as to the main house. The precise location of the service range was largely determined by custom and practice, based on the overriding principle that while it should be easily accessible to the main house, it should not intrude on the sensibilities of its occupants. The processes and activities taking place in the service range were not to be seen, heard or smelled by those it served.

There were three basic types of service range; they could form a wing of the main house, be placed in a basement or semi-basement beneath it, or they could be built around a separate courtyard. Llanerchaeron, Newton House, Alltyrodyn and Nanteos are all examples of courtyard ranges, while Ffynone is an example of a basement or semi-basement range, and Cilwendeg is an example of a service range in a wing of the main house.

Fig 6. Aerial view of Picton Castle showing the service range to the rear built around a courtyard.

The benefits of the basement plan were its close proximity to the household it served, and the fact that the overall symmetry of the façade was retained, thereby enhancing its visual appeal. Placing the service range in a wing of the house could make the house appear larger and more impressive. Furthermore, in theory at least, food could be delivered more quickly, and therefore be much warmer when served than if carried up a flight of stairs from the kitchen to the dining room. The advantages of the courtyard range were that it was largely separate from the house and posed less of a fire risk to the main house – an important consideration given the number of open fires, coppers and boilers in use in the service range at any one time. A courtyard plan also benefited from more daylight, less cramped conditions, and a more logically structured layout. The disadvantage was that it could be visually intrusive. To overcome that problem, service ranges were generally tucked away behind the house, and shielded from view by trees and shrubs. Even courtyard service ranges were rarely totally detached from the main house; the kitchen, servants' hall, butler's pantry and housekeeper's room still generally formed part of the main house, with only the dairy, brew house, laundry and bake house placed around the courtyard. Middleton Hall was slightly unusual in having a covered corridor linking the detached service range to the main house, while at Nanteos something of a mixture of types emerged over time. In the original Georgian house, as was normal, the kitchen formed part of the ground floor of the main house, but other elements of the service range, such as the laundry, bakery and brew house, were housed on a sort of ad hoc basis in separate buildings. It was only in the nineteenth century, following the enlargement of the house, that the service range became more structurally linked to the house. Courtyard service ranges generally had covered walkways around the interior, so that the servants could stay dry when moving between rooms in the rain. Beer and wine cellars were almost invariably placed beneath the main house, for coolness, security and convenience, and so that the butler could supervise and oversee them.

Whichever layout was chosen, it was carefully designed to ensure that the servants could not watch the family and their guests at play or enjoying their outdoor leisure activities. Stevenson, a prominent Victorian architect, stated explicitly:

> Under no circumstances, of course, should the servants overlook the private life of the family…None of their windows should command the lawn or private garden (Stevenson, 1880, p.80).

Similarly, the relationship between the house and service range was designed so that, on both sides of the green-baize door, an element of privacy was built into the layout:

...the Servants' Department shall be separated from the main house, so that what passes on either side of the boundary shall be both invisible and inaudible to the other...(Kerr, 1864, pp.74-75).

Of course, those serving at table or as lady's maids or valets would inevitably pick up information about the likes, dislikes and peccadilloes of their masters and mistresses. And given that servants handled the clothes, bed linen and chamber pots of the gentry, there would have been few intimate aspects of the family's daily lives that remained completely hidden from members of the service range.

THE KITCHEN

Fig 9. The kitchen at St Fagans showing the smoke-jack roasting range on the right of the picture and the dog spit in the centre.

Within the service range, the kitchen and scullery were of central importance, not only in terms of preparing and cooking food, but also in providing the entire household with hot water. In modest, country houses without a servants' hall, the kitchen was also where indoor servants met and relaxed when their chores were completed. In grander houses, servants' halls were provided so that they could socialise without being surrounded by their work.

The ability to prepare and produce high-quality food, and to serve that food quickly and efficiently to a large number of guests, was essential to the ethos of country-house living. Food achieved two of the gentry's key aims: pleasure and prestige. It provided pleasure in the form of gastronomic delights for the family, their friends and visitors, and prestige in the provision of lavish and generous hospitality. Of course, much depended on the skill of the cook, the way the kitchen was equipped, and the availability of provisions from the kitchen garden, home farm and wider estate.

Georgian and Victorian architects devoted a surprisingly large amount of attention to the design, location and orientation of kitchens. Where possible, kitchens were placed on the cooler, north-facing side of the house and had large windows, which when opened helped prevent the heat from roasting ranges, baking ovens and coppers becoming overpowering. Although kitchens and sculleries had to be well ventilated, the windows and doors had to be placed so that there was no danger of cooking smells entering the main house. The Welsh gentry may have enjoyed their food, but they didn't particularly enjoy the smell and noise of it being prepared.

The primary and essential function of the kitchen was, of course, to produce food for the table. That involved roasting and boiling meat, baking bread, making pies and pastries, and preparing vegetables. An associated function, though one usually carried out in the scullery, was washing the mountains of pots, pans, cutlery and crockery needed when the gentry entertained. The scullery was also often used for cleaning, preparing and cooking fish and vegetables.

Roast meat played a particularly important part in the gentry's diet and the centrepiece of any eighteenth-century kitchen was its roasting range – a means of roasting meat by slowly turning it on a spit in front of a large open fire. Turning the spit by hand was one of the least pleasant tasks in a kitchen because it involved standing for long periods of time close to the searing heat of the fire. To ease that problem, a number of technical devices were introduced into country-house kitchens to achieve the desired aim of roasting a haunch of meat without at the same time roasting a kitchen maid. There were three main ways of doing so: the smoke jack, the dog spit and the bottle jack.

Fig 7. The smoke-jack fan, St Fagans.

Smoke jacks used the rising heat from the fire to turn a fan in the chimney. The fan then turned the roasting spit, via a system of gears and line-shafting. A smoke jack was installed in the kitchen at Stradey in 1821(Stradey Archives, MS. 1651), and there were smoke jacks at St Fagans and Nanteos. There were undoubtedly many more in Welsh country houses, but evidence of them is now, unfortunately, missing. One of the minor technical problems of smoke jacks was that the combination of heat, smoke and soot in the chimney caused its internal moving parts to seize up, and the mechanism had to be frequently cleaned and greased. The smoke jack at Nanteos, for example, was regularly serviced by the local blacksmith (NLW 11106D).

Another problem with smoke jacks was that, in order to turn the spit, even when roasting small joints of meat, the fire often had to be fiercer than was absolutely necessary for the job in hand. That problem was overcome by the use of dog spits.

Dog spits were driven by a dog working a small treadmill fixed to the wall above the range. As the

Fig 8. The dog spit at St Fagans.

dog walked in the treadmill, it turned the spit. Again, quantifying the number in use within the region is difficult because subsequent changes

Fig 10. A Dutch oven, St Fagans.

to kitchens tended to eliminate all evidence of them. However, dog spits were definitely used at Plas Llangoedmor in Cardiganshire (Vaughan,[1926] 1988, p.17), and in the kitchen at St Fagans. However, dog spits were of course only capable of turning relatively small joints of meat, and required a trained dog.

Another way of roasting small joints of meat was by bottle jacks, so-called because they were the size and shape of a bottle. They were driven by clockwork, and once they were wound, they turned the meat suspended beneath them slowly in front of the fire. They were often used in conjunction with Dutch ovens – half-round shields, polished on the inside to reflect the heat back onto the joint being roasted. An additional advantage of using a Dutch oven was that at least some of the heat from the fire was deflected away from the kitchen interior.

By placing them on wall brackets, bottle jacks could also be used in front of small open fires and enclosed kitchen ranges. The closeness of the meat to the fire was adjusted by moving the jack back and forth along the arm of the wall bracket.

Roast meat, even in country houses, formed only a part of the normal daily diet, however. Bread, on the other hand, was a staple food and bake ovens were an essential feature of any country-house kitchen. They were also used to bake pies, puddings and cakes, and therefore provided a host of culinary delights for the tables of the gentry. Although small bake ovens were included in most kitchens, in large households they would rarely have been able to

Fig 11. The bake oven, with fire grate and metal doors, set within the original bake oven at Llanerchaeron.

keep up with all the demands placed on them, and so totally separate bake houses were provided – as at Llanerchaeron, Nanteos, and Newton House. There were many advantages of a separate bake house. First, concentrating the bulk of the baking activities in a separate building allowed the kitchen proper, to operate more efficiently. Second, it helped reduce the amount of heat in the kitchen. Finally, although baking bread took place only about twice a week, baking in bulk required a lot of space for equipment and materials. Large amounts of flour and grain needed to be stored somewhere, along with the large wooden troughs and bowls used for mixing the dough. A separate bake house was the ideal solution.

Traditional bake ovens were large, long chambers enclosed in clay or brick. They had a flue leading to a chimney, and were heated by lighting faggots of dry sticks inside the oven. When the faggots had burnt away and sufficient heat had been built up in the surrounding brickwork, the embers were scraped out and the loaves of proven (risen) dough were placed inside. The oven was then sealed with wooden doors and wet clay until the bread had been given enough time to bake. That of course required great skill and judgement, learnt only by trial and error, and it was still not an exact science. Later advances in the design of bake ovens involved building separate fire grates beneath the oven, and fixing metal doors to it. At a stroke, those improvements ensured greater control over the whole process, and greater ease in loading and unloading the oven.

Fig 12. The bake oven in the scullery at Llanerchaeron, along with an additional enclosed stove.

In the nineteenth century, the use of separate bake houses slowly went into decline. This was possibly a reflection of a slight change in the role of bread as part of the daily diet, as well as the growing use of enclosed kitchen ranges incorporating bread ovens. Even so, small bread ovens were sometimes provided in the kitchens and sculleries to supplement the kitchen range when the need arose.

The final nail in the coffin of the service-range bake house was the growth – especially in the early twentieth century – of commercial bakeries and retailers willing and able to deliver to outlying areas.

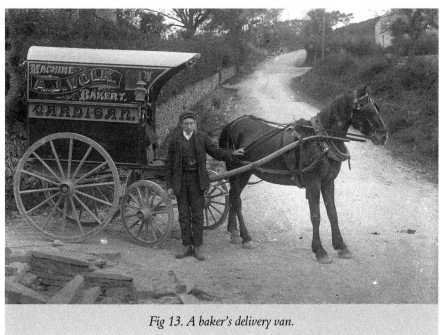

Fig 13. A baker's delivery van.

In addition to roasting meat and baking bread, the other key kitchen activities involved boiling vegetables, meat and fish. Traditionally that was done in large iron cauldrons hung over open fires, but later, the cauldrons were enclosed in brickwork, with built-in fire-grates placed beneath them, and flues to carry away the smoke and fumes. Such cauldrons were called 'coppers' primarily because the best ones were made of copper, though ultimately many 'coppers' were actually made of iron. As well as boiling vegetables and meat, coppers were also used extensively to heat water for use in the kitchen, scullery, laundry and bake house, and to provide the family with hot water for washing and bathing.

In addition to the standard fare of roast meat, boiled vegetables, fish and game, sauces added variety and flavour to meals. However, they needed to be prepared slowly and carefully over a very gentle heat, rather than over an open fire. Before the introduction of enclosed kitchen ranges with hobs capable of simmering food, the easiest and most reliable way of preparing sauces was on charcoal stoves. Charcoal stoves were able to provide moderate heat, with the added advantage of doing so without creating too much smoke. Unfortunately, that led some country-house owners to install them without troubling to connect them to a suitable flue. The problem was that although charcoal stoves didn't produce much smoke, they did produce copious amounts of carbon monoxide. In poorly ventilated kitchens, that could lead to some kitchen staff fainting from carbon-monoxide poisoning.

Charcoal stoves were also used for stewing and simmering food, but along with the roasting ranges, bread ovens and coppers, they added still more to the overall heat generated in a country-house kitchen, even when all the windows, doors and vents were wide open.

Fig 14. A copper in the kitchen at Llanerchaeron. The photograph shows the fire grate, and below it the ash box. On the right is the brass tap for drawing off hot water.

Fig 15. The charcoal stove, Llanerchaeron. At Llanerchaeron the charcoal stove was connected to a flue.

Fig 16. The cast-iron charcoal stove at Nanteos was placed beneath an opening window, but there is no obvious evidence of there being a flue to take the carbon-monoxide fumes away.

Hospitality and entertaining remained a key feature of country-house living throughout the Georgian, Victorian and Edwardian periods. Lavish dinners played an important part in that hospitality, and it was not unusual for eighteen or twenty guests to sit down to a five or six-course meal. It was therefore important that the kitchen and dining room were close enough together to allow the food to be carried from the kitchen to the dining room as quickly as possible, and served while it was still piping hot. At the same time, however, it was also necessary to ensure that cooking smells and kitchen noise were not noticeable in the dining room. Kitchens almost invariably formed part of the main house rather than being consigned to the exterior courtyard service range, and the corridors and passageways between the kitchen and dining room were kept as short as possible, but with intervening doors to reduce the risk of kitchen smells permeating the rest of the house. Serveries located between the kitchen and dining room were also a common feature of the room layout of many country houses, adding significantly to the speed and efficiency with which food could be served.

When kitchens were in the basement of country houses, hoists (dumb waiters) were sometimes installed to speed the delivery of meals. They saved having to carry food laboriously along corridors and up the backstairs to the dining-room servery. In essence, dumb waiters were

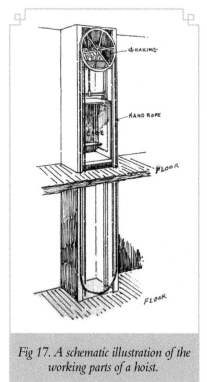

Fig 17. A schematic illustration of the working parts of a hoist.

Fig 18. The hand-cranked kitchen hoist at Ffynone.

moveable platforms, capable of carrying relatively light loads between floors using muscle power. They generally worked on a continuous rope-loop system or, as at Ffynone, a crank handle.

Given the vagaries of the speed at which dinner guests ate their food, and the capriciousness of kitchen ranges, the logistics of ensuring that food was served piping hot, and without delay, was, to say the least, quite challenging.

One way of keeping food hot until it was ready to be served was by using the hobs on charcoal stoves, or by using hot closets and hot plates in the servery or kitchen. Hot closets were heated by fire grates. The food was kept warm by the flues from the grate circulating around the inner, sealed chamber of the closet. The inner chamber was sealed to prevent the food being tainted by the fumes circulating around it.

Another way of keeping food warm in the servery was by the use of an additional stove. The one proposed for the servery at Stackpole Court in the 1840s included a warm-air system to provide additional heat in the dining room. In the proposed system, the stove would have heated the hob as well as a hot-air chamber behind the fire grate. As the air in the chamber warmed up, it would have passed through ducting into the adjacent dining room. The primary aim of the installation was to keep the food and plates warm, and the system would only have supplemented other forms of heating in the dining room. It is unclear whether or not the stove was ever actually installed, however (Letters, dated Jan 1841 and July 1841, Box 236 A, Cawdor Archives).

Fig 19. The hot closet in the kitchen at Nanteos.

Without doubt, the most significant advance in kitchen technology came in the nineteenth century with the development of the enclosed kitchen range or 'Kitchener'. Kitcheners were made of cast iron and incorporated hobs, ovens and back boilers into a single, though very substantial, piece of kitchen equipment. The fire grate was significantly smaller than the open fire of a roasting range, and was therefore both more efficient and economical. The main technical advance, however, was the way the flues were designed so that the heat from the fire could be directed, as required, to the ovens, back boiler and hobs, before passing into the chimney. Another improvement was the 'register door', which could be used to adjust the draught and, hence, the fierceness of the fire. Kitchen ranges not only helped reduce the overall amount of heat in a kitchen, but also provided a much more responsive and compact way of cooking.

Meat and vegetables could be boiled, fried and simmered on the range, dispensing with the need for coppers and stewing stoves. Bread, pies and pastries could be baked in the oven, dispensing with the need for separate baking ovens. The range could also be used to boil kettles for small amounts of water (for making tea, etc.), and the boilers incorporated in many ranges provided sufficient hot water for washing and shaving. Careful use of bottle jacks also allowed small joints to be roasted in front of the fire grate. In gentry households, therefore, the kitchen range, almost at a stroke, did away with all the coppers, bread ovens, stewing stoves and roasting ranges previously seen as necessary.

Although enclosed kitchen ranges were undoubtedly a huge help to hard-pressed kitchen staff, they could still be quite temperamental and needed skill, familiarity and expertise to get the temperatures just right for the specific job in hand (even the most advanced models didn't have

Fig 20. The nineteenth-century kitchen range at Nanteos, along with the bottle jacks used for roasting small joints in front of the fire-grate.

thermostatic controls). They also needed to be black-leaded every day to prevent the cast-iron rusting. And while they were more efficient and economical than open ranges, they still used up to a ton and a half of coal each month. They were also rarely capable of heating the quantities of water needed for bathing in an average household, especially if the family and house guests were all clamouring for baths at the same time. In such circumstances, coppers and independent boilers continued to be used.

While hoists were installed in some country houses to move food from the basement kitchen to the ground-floor dining room, it was not just food that had to be carried about the house. Coal, luggage, linen, slops, water for washing and bathing also had to be carried along corridors and between floors. Although some of those tasks were done by footmen or the odd-job man (the odd man), they mostly fell to the housemaids' lot.

All that labour-intensive movement of goods up and down the backstairs could have been eased considerably by the installation of service lifts and hoists, but, apart from the few dumb waiters already mentioned, only Middleton Hall appears to have installed a full-blown service lift (Vaughan, [1926] 1988, p.109). One of the problems of installing large-capacity lifts in country houses was that until the development of electric motors and the availability of a suitable electricity supply, they were not really feasible.

The burden of carrying coal and linen to the farthest extremities of a country house was sometimes, at least partially, eased by the use of staging posts. At Stackpole Court, for example, the odd man carried buckets of coal from the coal yard to designated coal closets throughout the house, leaving the housemaids to carry it from the coal closets to the various fireplaces. Stevenson, writing in 1880, stated:

> A *coal-closet* on every floor, or a chest which will hold a considerable supply in each housemaid's closet, which is filled by the men who bring in the coals, is a great saving of servants' labour, avoiding the necessity of carrying up the daily supply for the bedrooms and upper rooms…It should enter off the servants' stair, so that the dust rising from filling it should not get about the house (Stevenson, 1880, p.98).

Similarly, linen closets were provided on bedroom corridors so that fresh linen was always readily at hand when needed, and so that the process of changing bedsheets and towels could be completed quickly and efficiently.

If, due to age, injury or infirmity, members of the family were unable to climb the stairs to their bedrooms, they were carried there by their servants. At Nanteos, for example, William Powell, who was paralysed for the last twenty-years of his life, had wheelchairs on each floor of the house, but had to be carried between floors by his servants.

THE LAUNDRY

The rural elite obviously expected clean underclothes, spotless white tablecloths and table-napkins, and scrupulously clean bedsheets and towels. They also expected their female servants to wear starched white aprons, cuffs and caps. Those various demands generated huge amounts of soiled linen each week – much of it white, some needing to be starched, and all of it needing to be washed, dried and ironed. The laundry was, therefore, an essential part of any country-house service range.

The basic requirements for a laundry were quite simple; there needed to be a convenient and ample supply of clean water, coppers for heating the water and boiling the whites, a means of scrubbing wet linen, facilities to dry it and, finally, some way of ironing it. The washing was generally done in a separate wash house called the wet laundry, and it was starched and ironed in the dry laundry (Sambrook, 1999, p.154). In west Wales, the laundry technology was rarely as extensive as in some of the grander houses of England; it was somewhat more 'domestic' in scale. Even so, specific rooms in the service range were normally set aside for the two distinctly separate processes of washing and ironing. Nanteos, Newton House and Llanerchaeron all had separate, quite sophisticated laundry facilities.

In the wet laundry, a copper would be used to heat the water and to boil whatever needed to be boiled. There would also be washing troughs and tubs for scrubbing soiled linen. At Llanerchaeron, while the dry laundry (ironing) room is well documented and remains in its original position, there is no evidence of there ever being a permanent wet laundry or washhouse. The assumption is that the adjacent brew house (and the smallest of the three coppers within it) was used as the wet laundry. Such a system was not at all unusual, as Pamela Sambrook states:

'...the single most common place where washing equipment was kept was the brew house and it seems reasonable to suppose that fixed equipment for boiling liquor or worts could also be used heating water for laundry; brewing manuals often mentioned this practice, albeit with horror' (Sambrook, 1999, p.153).

Fig 21. The copper in the brew house at Llanerchaeron, probably used as the copper for the wet laundry.

Nanteos was built at about the same time as Llanerchaeron and a similar approach was adopted there, with the dry laundry placed over the brew house. Because brewing beer was an intermittent process, with careful scheduling, the same building could easily be used for both.

At Cilwendeg, the laundry was in a building completely separate from the main house, and though there is little surviving evidence of its internal layout, the wet laundry would have been on the ground floor with the dry laundry immediately above it. The wet and dry laundries at Newton House were separate buildings, forming part of the service range courtyard.

After being washed, and then mangled to remove as much water as possible, the laundry needed to be dried. Ideally, that would be done outdoors on nearby drying grounds, where the sun would help bleach the whites, and where the wind would give the clothes and bedding a fresh, wholesome smell. Given the damp climate of west Wales, however, it was important to have some form of back-up drying system. That could take the form of heated drying cabinets or, more commonly, indoor clothes horses, as at Llanerchaeron. In his book *House Architecture*, J.J. Stevenson in discussing laundries stated:

Fig 22. The dry laundry at Llanerchaeron.

'The Laundry…is used for ironing and dressing the clothes, and where there is no drying closet or loft for the purpose, for drying them in winter and wet weather. In that case it should be high in the ceiling, so that the clothes may be hung up above the head on horses raised by pulleys. It should have a wide table in good light for ironing; a stove for heating the irons, the heat from which serves also to dry the clothes' (Stevenson, 1880, p.99).

It is noteworthy that not all country houses had permanent, living-in laundry maids. Instead, it was quite common for women from the estate cottages or nearby villages to come in and undertake that role over a number of days each week. Living-in staff tended to be those who might be called upon at any time of the day or night, and laundry maids didn't really fall into that category.

THE BREW HOUSE

Beer was consumed in vast quantities by the gentry, as well as by their domestic servants and estate workers. It was a key element of a servant's daily requirement (an important part of board wages), and it was also seen as part of the gentry's largesse at celebrations and festivities held on the estate for members of staff, estate workers and the wider community. Beer was also provided as a reward for unusually heavy or unpleasant tasks such as collecting and stacking ice in the ice house or emptying cesspits. Brewing beer was therefore an important service-range activity in many Welsh country houses. Varying strengths of beer were brewed, with the stronger 'ales' kept primarily for the gentry, and the somewhat weaker brews (small beer) provided for servants and children. During the eighteenth century, and for much of the nineteenth century, beer was almost the only beverage, and was drunk during meals throughout the day – even at breakfast.

Beer was of course also drunk extensively purely for pleasure, relaxation and celebration. It was brewed commercially in towns and cities, as well as in many rural inns and taverns. It was also brewed for personal consumption in private houses, farms and cottages. Because of their isolation, and the large quantities of beer needed, most country houses brewed their beer in bulk. Alltyrodyn Mansion, Nanteos, Newton House, Llanerchaeron and Stradey all had brew houses. They were generally found in the service-range complex, though far enough away from the main house to prevent the smell of the brewing process causing offence 'the Brew house itself ought to be so placed that its vapours shall not penetrate into and around the House' (Kerr, 1864, p.267).

Although brewing beer was quite a straightforward process, it still required great skill to get the strength and taste just right, and there were many variables that could prove disastrous in inexperienced hands. The basic ingredients needed to brew beer were water, malted barley, hops and yeast. Hops and barley were not widely grown in the region, so they had to be brought in from other parts of Britain. In Welsh brew houses, the first stage in the brewing process was milling (grinding) the malted barley. After that, the milled malt was 'mashed' by mixing it with water

Fig 23. The mash tuns at Llanerchaeron.

and heated for several hours in a mash tun (a large copper). That produced the 'wort', which was removed from the tun and strained to remove any sediment. It was then returned to the mash tun, where hops were added and the mixture was boiled for several more hours. After that, the liquor was strained to remove the hops and then allowed to cool in shallow trays. When cool, it was placed in a fermenting tun, yeast was added, and it was then left for several days to ferment.

After fermenting, the beer was run off into barrels and left to settle (sometimes with the help of 'finings' to help it clear). The barrels were then stored in the cool of beer cellars where the butler could keep an eye on them. At Alltyrodyn Mansion and Newton House, as much space was devoted to the beer cellars as to the wine cellars. From start to finish, the brewing process took six or seven days, with up to sixteen hours of intense activity taking place on the first day (Sambrook, 1996, pp.18-19). Brewing was, however, undertaken only intermittently, generally in autumn, winter and spring.

Fig 24. The beer cellar at Llanerchaeron.

Country-house brewing went into decline in the second half of the nineteenth century (Sambrook, 1996, p.249), largely due to tea becoming the more universally popular daytime drink. The changeover from beer to tea was also strongly influenced in Wales by the growth of Methodism and teetotalism. Furthermore, as the century progressed, tea became cheaper and was seen as more refreshing and refined. The decline of estate brew houses accelerated still further with the growth of commercial brewers, and better transport links. For country-house owners, purchasing beer from commercial suppliers had a lot of appeal. It was of a consistent quality and strength; it could be bought and delivered whenever it was required; and it didn't tie up manpower or require the provision and upkeep of specialist equipment. It also marked a shift in the gentry's preference for evening consumption, away from beer and ale to spirits and wine (fortified or otherwise).

THE DAIRY

Before the widespread commercial production of butter, cream and cheese, country houses relied almost entirely on their own resources to produce such goods. Milk was readily available from the home farm, but the work of turning it into butter, cream and cheese was carried out in the service range. The processes involved required carefully designed buildings, tailored specifically for dairying, and appropriate fixtures and fittings. It was essential to create a cool, sterile environment, and, where possible, dairies were built facing north, with extensive eaves to shade the building from the sun. The interiors were tiled, and slate was used extensively, both for ease of cleaning and for the coolness it provided. Cleanliness was essential for the successful production of cheese, butter and cream, and most of the equipment and surfaces had to be sterilised before use.

Fig 25. The former dairy at Nanteos, with large, overhanging eaves for coolness.

Fig 26. The cheese press at Llanerchaeron.

Cheese was an important part of the diet in the eighteenth and nineteenth centuries. It was made by curdling milk with rennet (part of the lining of a calf's stomach), to form curds and whey. The curds were then separated from the whey and drained, before as much of the remaining liquid as possible was squeezed out using a cheese press. The resultant cheese was then left to mature.

To make butter, the cream from fresh milk was separated from the milk by leaving it in pans for about twenty-four hours before skimming it off the top. The cream was then left for a further two or three days, and then placed in a butter churn. There were two types of churn; one was simply a tall wooden vessel with a plunger; the other type was essentially a wooden barrel on a stand, with a handle attached to the barrel. In the plunger-type churn, the plunger was forced up and down inside the churn until the butter had 'come'. In the barrel type, the handle either turned paddles within the churn, or the whole barrel was rotated until the butter came.

Fig 27. A butter churn and plunger at Llanerchaeron.

Fig 28. A butter worker at Llanerchaeron used to squeeze any excess liquid out of the butter.

The butter was then washed, and any remaining moisture was forced out using a 'butter worker', an inclined, shallow wooden tray with a drain hole at the lower end to allow liquid to escape. The butter was 'worked' by running the hand-cranked roller up and down over it, to squeeze out any liquid. Butter pats were then used to form the butter into suitably-sized blocks.

As with many other service-range activities, butter, cream and cheese-making went into decline with the growth of commercial dairies and retailers willing to deliver to outlying areas.

Fig 29. The Llandeilo Butter and Cheese Factory.

SERVANTS' BELLS

There was self-evidently little point in having servants if they couldn't be summoned easily. The final element of service-range technology to be discussed here is the use of servants' bells. In modest country houses, servants could be called simply by their master or mistress ringing a hand bell or by shouting for them. As houses grew in size and scale, those were no longer viable options and, instead, pull-cord systems of servants' bells were installed. Pull cords were placed in all the principal rooms of the house, connected by wires and pulleys to a bell board in the service range. The bells were marked to indicate which room was calling for attention. Because the bells were on flexible springs they carried on shaking long after they had been rung, which allowed servants to know which room to attend, for some time after the bell had initially been rung. Some installations even had different sized bells so that the sound differed between them, and servants could tell just by listening to them, which room they had to attend. Although most country houses eventually had bell pulls, the number of rooms served by them could be quite limited. The 1829 inventory for Stradey, for example, listed bell pulls in the Old Drawing Room and the dining room, though not in any of the bedrooms or the breakfast parlour. At Ffynone, as late as 1874, the only bell pulls were in the drawing room, study and the three main bedrooms.

In theory, bell-pull systems were simple and straightforward, but in practice they were difficult to install in large, rambling houses. They also sometimes malfunctioned due to the wires stretching, becoming tangled, or unhinged. Even so, bell-pull systems were used in most country houses across Wales, sometimes with a particularly fine range of bells – as at Alltyrodyn Mansion. It can be argued that the widespread use of servants' bells in country houses ultimately symbolised the divorce between family and servants, and the fact that it would have been inconceivable for members of the family to undertake even quite trivial tasks for themselves, or to personally seek out a servant to give him or her their instructions.

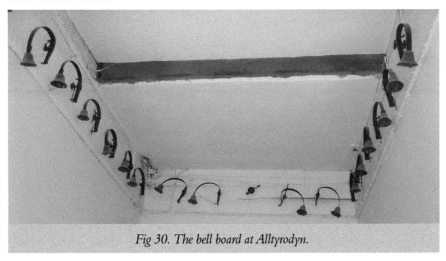

Fig 30. The bell board at Alltyrodyn.

In the late-nineteenth and early-twentieth centuries, there was a gradual shift from bell pulls to electric bell pushes due to the introduction of electricity in many Welsh country houses. Although electricity was introduced primarily to provide electric lighting, its use for calling servants was quickly recognised, and electric bell boards quickly began to replace the old bell-board system. Electric bell pushes were less likely to malfunction and get tangled up. As with the old, bell-board system, room-indicators in the bell-box continued to show which room was calling for attention, long after the bell had been run, in some cases until a reset button had been pressed. Electric bell pushes were also ideally suited to the battery storage system adopted by most country houses.

Internal telephone systems would have been even more efficient of course, because instructions could be given without a servant having to first

Fig 31. The electric bell board at Ffynone.

make their way to the room in question. While telephones linked to the outside world were welcomed in country houses, as with many other forms of technology, the roll-out to country estates was slow due to the distances involved. Furthermore, the network was patchy and intermittent, and before the 1920s few rural exchanges operated at night or on Sundays. Even so, telephones in country houses grew in popularity in the inter-war period with, for example, both Nanteos and Bronwydd installing them in 1926. For those living in isolated parts of the country, the telephone provided the ideal means of communicating not only with friends and relatives, but also with tradesmen and suppliers.

In summary, between 1750 and 1930, major technological changes took place in country houses, leading to a marked reduction in the number of activities taking place in the service range. The growth of commercial laundries, breweries and bakeries meant that the need for the full panoply of service-range activities became largely unnecessary, and retailers were more than willing to travel out to country houses to provide whatever goods were required – a trend made easier by the use of motorised goods vehicles, better roads and telephones.

With the introduction of electricity in Welsh country houses, especially in the inter-war period, there was a growing use of electrical appliances. While such appliances had been available from the late-nineteenth century, the take-up in country houses was severely limited, largely because most independent country-house installations were small in scale, and would have been unable to run many of the appliances available – even if there had been a desire to do so. It was only due to declining servant numbers in the inter-war period that the Welsh gentry began to see the appeal of electrical appliances in their homes. They did so because they increasingly found that they had to undertake for themselves many of the domestic chores they had previously thought beneath them. That trend grew after the Second World War, encouraged by the spread of the National Grid and high-voltage, alternating current electricity into rural areas.

WATER SUPPLY

Bathing may not have been a particularly high priority for the Welsh squirearchy in the eighteenth century, but the overall comfort and convenience of the gentry household was certainly dependent on an ample supply of water. In addition to the admittedly quite limited amounts required for personal hygiene, water was needed for cooking and preparing meals, for brewing beer and for laundry work. Water was also needed for the stables. When horses and horse-drawn vehicles were the only means of transport, stabling a large number of horses was a necessity. Nanteos and Alltyrodyn Mansion had extensive stables, while at Middleton Hall over twenty horses were regularly stabled. On average horses drink between 5 and 10 gallons of water a day, so the total amount of water needed, just for the stables, was quite significant.

Given its undoubted importance, access to a reliable and plentiful water supply was a vitally important consideration when planning the location of any new country house, which is why many were initially built on low-lying ground close to rivers, or where shallow wells could meet their day-to-day demands. Stradey, for example, was built more or less on a flood plain, while both the original Tudor house at Ffynone and the somewhat later Aberglasney were built directly over shallow wells. Building houses close to watercourses had the added advantage of making wastewater disposal more convenient – it was simply discharged back into them, though, of course, downstream. In the nineteenth century, when it became fashionable to build or relocate country houses on higher ground, the ability to supply them with water was often a major factor determining the viability of such schemes.

The heavy rainfall, and the abundant streams, rivers and springs that are such a feature of west Wales, meant that the Welsh gentry were generally in a very favourable position when it came to water supply. They could often obtain sufficient supplies by gravity-feed, rather than by building reservoirs or having to adopt expensive pumping systems. Alltyrodyn Mansion, Stradey Castle, Nanteos, (and ultimately Ffynone) all gained their water supply by gravity-feed from nearby hills.

In the eighteenth century, water from springs and streams would normally be channelled into large, lead-lined slate cisterns close to the service range, and rainwater from the roofs of buildings could also be fed into them if required. In other cases, water was drawn from shallow wells, dug by hand and lined with stone. Shallow wells provided an ideal, low-tech way of gaining a suitably adequate water supply capable of meeting the needs of most country houses. Having dug the well, all that was then needed was a bucket on a rope or a hand-pump. A water trough was usually placed next to the well, and water was pumped or bucketed into

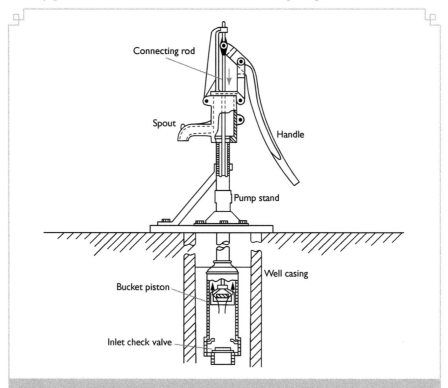

Fig 32. Schematic illustration of a hand pump. Atmospheric pressure forced water into a cylinder on the up stroke of the pump. The inlet valve then closed, and on the down stroke the water was forced out of the cylinder via the outlet pipe.

it several times a day, so that water was always available when needed. While meeting the day-to-day demands for water in country houses in the eighteenth century was relatively easy, that changed dramatically in the nineteenth century due to the growing emphasis on bathing and personal cleanliness, and the fashion for wealthy landowners to relocate their existing properties to higher ground. That often meant obtaining an adequate water supply from shallow wells or nearby watercourses became much more of a problem, and many landowners were forced to augment their supplies by sourcing their water from higher

Fig 33. A kitchen maid drawing water using a double-acting hand pump in the service-range courtyard at Alltyferin (Courtesy of Carmarthen Museum Service).

ground, and from further afield. Fortunately, technological progress in hydraulic engineering in the eighteenth and nineteenth centuries helped overcome the twin problems of increasing demand and less easy access.

Although few landowners in west Wales built large-scale reservoirs, many impounded water behind weirs to meet their day-to-day demands. They also often used large additional storage tanks to ensure continuity of supply. In the 1880s, for example, the owners of Alltyrodyn Mansion built a weir on nearby farmland above the house and then piped the water from the weir to a covered settlement tank from where it was piped to the house by gravity feed. Weirs were significantly smaller, cheaper and easier to build than reservoirs. In principle, they needed only a bank of stone to be thrown across a convenient stream to impound the water behind to form a sort of millpond. Water was then carried from the weir in conduits to wherever it was needed. When the weir was full, the excess water simply flowed over the top of the weir (via the spillway) back into the river or stream below.

Fig 34. The weir at Ffynone (formerly used to provide water for the hydroelectric scheme).

Constructing a weir needed only very basic building skills, and although silting could be something of a problem, it was easily overcome by regular dredging. Weirs were used not only to supply water to the service range and stables, but could also be used to supply ornamental fountains, fire hydrants, and ultimately hydroelectric schemes. Country-house owners could also exploit them to create water features, or use them as boating lakes, etc.

In the eighteenth century, the conduits carrying the water were generally made of elm trunks, hollowed out and joined together with clay. They simply carried water to storage cisterns close to, but outside, the service range. The flow was not controlled, and any excess would normally be channelled into one of the house drains. Although lead for internal pipe work was used, it was expensive and most water for the service range was carried in buckets from outdoor cisterns. Large-scale, indoor plumbing in the service range and to the upper floors of country houses was more a feature of the second half of the nineteenth century. It was also in the second half of the nineteenth century that cast-iron pipes began to replace the wooden pipes previously used for carrying water to the service range.

Water from weirs, streams and rivers was used primarily for washing, cooking, cleaning and laundry work; it was rarely drunk in its natural state by the gentry. Instead, wherever possible, spring water was used. Lord Dynefor of Newton House, for example, had a supply of spring water piped to the house, solely for drinking and brewing beer. Spring water was prized not only for its taste and sparkling clarity, but also because it was free from the risk of animal contamination. Although the precise bacterial mechanism of disease transmission was not fully understood until the second half of the nineteenth century, the gentry were well aware of the health risks of drinking polluted water. If spring water was not available, the alternative was to filter it using domestic carbon filters. In any case, water in any form was not drunk to excess by the gentry in the eighteenth century.

The danger of drinking contaminated water was fully recognised, and was an obvious concern by the end of the nineteenth century. Apart from filtering it, one way of avoiding such risks, and of ensuring an adequate supply, was to store spring water in covered underground reservoirs, before piping it to the house. Ffynone, for example, adopted such a system in the early-1900s, when it began to draw its water from a spring on a hillside on the other side of the valley.

Fig 35. One of the two underground, spring-water storage reservoirs serving Ffynone.

For most of the eighteenth and nineteenth centuries, the service range was the primary user of water in country houses, and because service ranges were always built at or below ground level, channelling water into nearby cisterns using gravity feed or hand pumps presented few problems. It was also perfectly possible to provide limited, piped cold-water supplies to key rooms 'within' service ranges using gravity feed. In the nineteenth century, for example, Llanerchaeron had extensive piped water supplies throughout the service range, but it was not until 1906 that there was a piped water supply in the main house. Another example of the very partial use of piped water supplies in Welsh country houses is Stradey, where during a major refurbishment in the 1820s, although new lead pipes and stopcocks were provided leading from the cistern to the scullery and pantry, and a new house-drain was laid from the scullery to the river, piped water was not extended to the upper floors of the house (Stradey Archives, MS 1651, Carmarthenshire Archives Service). That reluctance on the part of country-house owners to install a piped supply to the bedrooms and cloakrooms of the main house was largely due to the fact that with ample servants to fetch and carry water, such a supply was deemed unnecessary. Such supplies were only needed when plumbed-in bathrooms and water closets became fashionable.

COUNTRY-HOUSE BATHROOMS

Although the Georgian gentry may not have been renowned for being overly fastidious, and while total immersion in a bath was not generally seen as an essential part of their daily routine, it would be wrong to suggest that they were entirely lax in their personal hygiene – far from it. Washing, though largely confined to the face, hands and feet, was an essential part of the morning ritual, and occasionally, for example after a day's hunting, they might even choose to soak the mud and sweat away in a hip bath.

The gentry of course washed and bathed in the warmth, comfort and privacy of their own bedrooms, and washstands and washbasins, water jugs, bidets, footbaths and hip baths were scattered liberally throughout country houses. In the principal bedrooms, washstands, washbasins and water jugs were elegant and decorative; they were designed to be both attractive and convenient to use. Their ownership was seen as a mark of a family's wealth and good taste, and their aesthetic

Fig 36. A washstand with chamber pot, washbowl and ewer.

appeal lingered on long into the nineteenth century. While evidence of the existence of washbowls and hip baths is not necessarily evidence of their use, it does show how personal cleanliness could be achieved, if it was desired. In addition, although total immersion in water was admittedly a fairly infrequent occurrence in Welsh country houses, there was always at least one hip bath to meet the family's requirements. The eighteenth-century reluctance to bathe was something of a hangover from previous centuries when bathing was deemed to be positively dangerous to health.

As with many elements of the gentry's daily routine, the morning's ablutions were intended to be as pleasurable an experience as possible. Hippolyte Taine, describing typical washing arrangements in a country house, wrote:

> In my bedroom, the entire floor is carpeted, a strip of oilcloth is in front of the washing-stand. There are two dressing-tables, each having two drawers, the first is provided with a swing looking-glass, the second is furnished with one large jug, one small one, a medium one for hot water, two porcelain basins, a dish for toothbrushes, two soap-dishes, a water-bottle with its tumbler, a finger-glass with its glass. Underneath is a very low table, a sponge, another basin, a large shallow zinc bath for morning bathing. (Taine, 1885, p.182).

His description closely mirrors the facilities provided in the bedrooms of Stradey Castle in the late-nineteenth century, when there was a mahogany washstand with associated basin, jug, hot water can, slop bucket and cover, and a large painted tin footbath in the principal bedroom (Inventory, Stradey Castle Archives, ML 2477, Carmarthenshire Archives Service).

Taine went on to describe the daily ritual, in which a servant would bring in 'a large can of hot water with a fluffy towel on which to place the feet' (Taine, 1885, p.183). Taine's description not only evokes a picture of the extent to which the gentry were pampered in the nineteenth century, but it also illustrates an important aspect of personal hygiene, that of taking a 'sponge-bath'. Sponge baths took various forms, from the very simple process of using a flannel to wash various parts of the body while standing in front of a washbowl, to actually standing in a sponge bath – the 'large shallow zinc bath' mentioned by Taine. Sponge baths were just shallow tinplate bowls about 3 feet wide, with a spout to make emptying them easier. They provided an ideal way of gaining overall cleanliness using only a minimal amount of water (Eveleigh, 2002, p.69). Taine's description of washing and bathing facilities in a country house also supports the view that even in the late-nineteenth century, traditional forms of washing and bathing continued to be viewed as perfectly acceptable, even luxurious. Much of the luxury of course depended on servants being able to provide sufficient hot water to meet the competing and simultaneous demands of members of the family and their guests. In 1866, Hermione Jennings complained in her journal that while visiting Pentre, a country house in

Manordeifi, 'they brought very small cans and the water barely warm' (Jennings, quoted in Jones, 1974, Vol XI, p.27).

In spite of the fact that there may occasionally have been inadequacies in the quality and quantity of the water supplied, the comfort and convenience of washing and bathing in one's own bedroom outweighed most of the system's weaknesses. As long as there were enough servants to undertake the chores involved, there was no obvious advantage in going to the expense of installing plumbed-in baths and washbasins, and a piped hot and cold water supply.

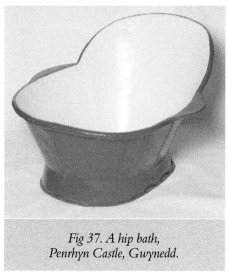

Fig 37. A hip bath,
Penrhyn Castle, Gwynedd.

The inventories for Stradey, and later for Stradey Castle, show that throughout the eighteenth and nineteenth centuries the Mansel Lewis family were totally reliant on washbasins, footbaths and hip baths for all their washing and bathing needs. All the family bedrooms had a washstand, washbasin and jug, footbath, chamber pot, slop bucket and hot water cans. Each bedroom also had a drinking glass and a bottle for drinking water, just in case the occupant felt thirsty in the middle of night when servants would no longer be available to bring refreshments. Some, though not all, of the bedrooms at Stradey also had hip baths and portable bidets. The fact that hip baths were not found in all the bedrooms is evidence first of their easy portability and, second, that it was more common to have a 'sponge bath' when it was felt necessary to do so.

An inventory for Golden Grove in 1821 shows that in addition to all the principal bedrooms and dressing rooms having the usual washstands, washbasins and water jugs, there were twelve portable bidets scattered throughout the various bedrooms, indicating a particularly heightened sense of personal hygiene. A hip bath, footbath and even a portable shower were also available (Golden Grove Inventory 1821, Carmarthenshire Archives Service).

The portable shower at Golden Grove is particularly interesting because it was made by a London manufacturer (Gideon Dare of Cockspur Street). In the eighteenth century, London was an important centre for the manufacture of luxury goods, as well as being a commercial, political and social centre. The Welsh gentry would frequently visit the capital, staying for long periods of time, and buy their luxury items there. Along with its shower curtains, steps, filling pot and carriage to Wales, the Golden Grove shower cost £7.00 in 1789 (equivalent to about £910 today) (Cawdor Muniments 28/2764, 16 May 1789, Carmarthenshire Archives Service). Portable showers grew in popularity during the nineteenth century; Old Bronwydd, for example, had two by the late-1840s (Baker-Jones, 2005, p.100). They were remarkably simple in operation. The reservoir above the shower was filled with either hot or cold water (depending on the washer's preference); the user would step into the shower, draw the curtains and open the valve to release the flow. The pump in the base was used to raise the

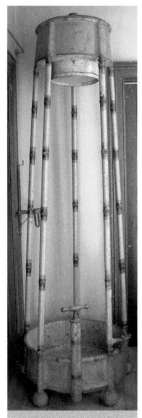

Fig 38. A portable shower bath.

water to the reservoir, and to pump out the waste water into a slop bucket.

In most country houses, the principal bedrooms had adjoining dressing rooms, and it was there that the washstand, footbath, hip bath, etc., would be kept, turning them virtually into en suite bathrooms. And it was there, of course, that washing, shaving and bathing took place. At Ffynone, for example, there were dressing rooms attached to the North, South and East bedrooms, and all had wash stands, washbasins and jugs (Inventory 1874, NLW). As bedrooms and dressing rooms were invariably heated by coal fires, even in the depths of winter washing, bathing and dressing remained pleasurable experiences. In the late-nineteenth century, despite more and more country houses installing plumbed-in bathrooms attached to the principal bedrooms, junior members of the family (and houseguests) still relied largely on washstands and portable hip baths to serve their needs. At Glaspant, for example, Henry Howell (the eldest son and heir) was still using a hip bath at the end of the nineteenth century, and even filled it himself if he wanted a bath before the servants were up and about. In his diary entry for 4 June 1896, he states, 'I got up at 3.30am & fetched hot water from the kitchen boiler for my bath; went out through smoking-room &…went fishing'. A few days later he wrote, 'I got up at 6am & got water from kitchen boiler for my bath' (Baker-Jones, 2001, pp.84-5). Not only do his diary entries indicate a cheerful willingness to fill his own bath, but they also show a keen desire to bathe on a daily basis.

Washing the face and hands in a wash bowl required very little water, and sponge baths simply used the same water. Even hip baths were remarkably efficient in terms of the quantity of water used, though the water still had to be carried from the service range to the bedrooms, and then had to be carried back downstairs after it had been used.

It was not until the late-nineteenth century that housemaid's closets on the upper floors of country houses began to be fitted with piped hot and cold water, and slop sinks leading to the house-drains (Quennell, in Weaver, 1912, p.103). They were a tremendous boon to the housemaids, making it far easier for them to clean and empty chamber pots, etc. It also made the task of delivering hot and cold water to bedrooms without a piped supply far less onerous. While it is fair to say that very few housemaids' closets were provided in Welsh country houses, Golden Grove was one of the few houses in west Wales that did provide them.

Pleasurable and convenient though it may have been to use a washstand and hip bath in front of an open fire in one's own private bedroom or dressing room, it was even more pleasurable to wash and bathe whenever the urge arose, and to use as much hot water as desired. It was that which led to the growth of plumbed-in bathrooms in the second half of the nineteenth century. One was even installed at Stackpole Court as early as 1830. Although Stackpole Court may have been at the forefront of bathroom provision at the time, other country houses soon followed suit. Newton House had bathrooms installed in the 1850s and Alltyrodyn Mansion had one in the late-1870s (Alltyrodyn sales catalogue, 1881).

The first bathroom in any country house was almost invariably installed in the dressing room of the principal bedroom, replacing the washstands, basins, ewers and hip baths previously used there. It was an overt sign of prestige, befitting the leading member of the household. The trend for more and more country houses to have plumbed-in bathrooms reflected changing fashions and expectations, and the abandonment of formerly accepted, though admittedly quite limited, standards of washing and bathing. The benefits of having a piped hot and cold water supply to one's own, personal bathroom were obvious. Piped hot water was more plentiful and warmer than water carried by hand from the service range; baths could be made larger and hold more water than hip baths, and the added bonus was that the bath could be topped-up with more hot water as and when required. Those factors combined to make it possible to linger longer, and enjoy an even more pleasant and luxurious experience than ever before.

Fashion, luxury and convenience, though of primary importance, weren't the only reasons for the move towards plumbed-in bathrooms, however. During the second half of the century, an admittedly erroneous theory emerged linking diseases such as cholera with the smell (miasma) of rotting waste, body odour and filth. As a consequence, elite members of society became almost obsessively fearful of the smell of dirt and grime. Bathing and personal hygiene took on a new significance and came to be seen as an essential part of a gentleman's daily regimen. By the opening years of the twentieth century, plumbed-in bathrooms had begun to be viewed as an essential feature of any country house with pretensions of luxury and style. At Ffynone, the dressing rooms of all the main bedrooms were converted into bathrooms in the early-twentieth century, and

in 1906 Cilwendeg had a bathroom attached to the master bedroom, along with one other bathroom and a water closet. Even Llanerchaeron, not generally at the fore in adopting new forms of domestic technology, converted one of the servants' bedrooms into a bathroom for use by Thomas Powell Lewes and his family in 1919.

Fig 39. The early-twentieth century bathroom at Llanerchaeron.

While it was increasingly taken for granted that there would be at least one bathroom in any country house (generally that linked to the master bedroom), most country houses retained traditional washing arrangements for guests and junior members of the family. That situation carried on well into the twentieth century. The exception to the rule was the nursery suite, which, being on the upper floor of the house and furthest away from the service range, often gained a piped hot and cold water supply at quite an early stage in the introduction of new technology.

The obvious prerequisites for a plumbed-in bathroom were hot and cold running water, and a suitable drainage system. As most bathrooms were installed on outside walls, drainage was quite simple; the wastewater pipes were simply carried through the outer wall of the house into soil pipes leading to the house drains.

Piped cold water was also relatively easy to provide; all that was needed was a cold-water supply to a storage tank at some point higher than the draw-off taps of the baths and washbowls it served. Where possible, the storage tank would be filled by gravity feed. If for some reason that was not an option, pumping had to be resorted to. Although hand pumps were quite capable of filling ground-level water cisterns from shallow wells, they were generally unable to pump water to the upper floors of country houses. A typical hand-pump could raise water only by about ten metres, sufficient to supply a ground level cistern. However, the deeper the well or the higher the cistern it served, the less likely it was to achieve satisfactory results. Even when a hand pump could reach the first floor of a country house, water would need to be pumped at least twice a day, for about two hours each time, just to meet normal daily demands. Hand pumping for multiple bathrooms and water closets was almost out of the question, especially if a large house party was being entertained. Hand pumping would then have been an almost continuous task and still would hardly have been able to keep up with demand.

Because hand pumping was so problematical, and because gravity-fed supplies were so readily available, there are very few examples in the region of hand-pumping water to the upper floors of country houses. However, though rare, it wasn't entirely unheard of. When Bodringallt (near Llawhaden in Pembrokeshire) was built in 1909, water was pumped by hand from a shallow well at the rear of the house to a storage tank on the first floor, from where it served the scullery, kitchen, and a single bathroom.

For country houses unable to obtain water by gravity feed, and where hand-pumping was impracticable, the only solution was large-scale mechanical pumping. Newton House provides a remarkably good example of the evolving nature of mechanised water supply in Wales. The house dates from 1660 and was built more-or-less on a flood plain, with water for the house being provided by ground-level storage cisterns near the service range. When the house was modernised in the nineteenth century, it was decided to supply the upper floors of the house with piped water. To do so, a false head of water was created using storage tanks on the hillside above the house. The outfall from the lake drove a waterwheel attached to a borehole pump, which pumped the water to the tanks. As the name implies, a borehole is produced by boring a deep shaft into the ground in order to access the extensive supplies of water in the strata below. Water from the Newton House storage tanks passed through filters before being carried by gravity to the bathrooms

Fig 40. The water wheel in the pump house at Newton House.

and water closets on the second-floor of the house. The storage tanks also supplied the service range with water. The waterwheel was supplemented by a diesel engine in the 1920s.

The drinking water at Newton House was entirely separate from the borehole supply. It was provided by a ram pump installed in 1900 to pump

Fig 43. The ram pump in the pump house at Newton House.

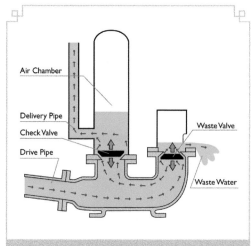

Fig 44. A schematic illustration of a ram pump.

spring water to a separate storage tank, from where it was piped to the main house. The advantage of the ram pump was that because it was driven by spring water, it didn't need a petrol engine or electric motor to be provided.

Ram pumps have just two moving parts, a spring-loaded waste valve and a check valve. As water flows down the drive pipe, the 'drag' effect of moving water closes the waste valve. The shock of the flow of water suddenly hitting the closed valve causes a back flush. The back flush then forces open the check valve, allowing water to enter the delivery pipe, while at the same time increasing the air pressure in the air chamber. That, in turn, sends water up the delivery pipe. As the flow into the delivery pipe slows, the check valve closes, and the spring-loaded waste valve opens, ready for the next cycle to begin.

The complete Newton House installation was extensive, expensive and sophisticated. On a smaller scale, petrol and diesel engines provided a

Fig 42. The diesel engine in the pump house at Newton House.

simple way of pumping water to the upper floors of country houses. Petrol engines linked to mechanical pumps were straightforward to install and easy to operate. The most widely used petrol engine for pumping water was the

Lister engine (manufactured by Lister and Co of Dursley). Lister engines were first produced in 1909, and were connected to mechanical water pumps by belt drive. They grew in popularity and the Lister Company not only manufactured its own pumps, but also produced combined, 'close-coupled' models, where the engine and pump were directly linked (that is without a belt drive). A fairly typical Lister pump could raise water from a 50-foot deep well to a height of 300 feet, and could pump between 300 and 400 gallons of water per hour.

Impressive though that might appear when compared to hand pumping, the pumping capacity of an electric pump was even more impressive. By the close of the nineteenth century, a 1,500-gallon tank could be filled in about 40 minutes. The obvious advantage a petrol engine had over an electric motor was that it didn't require a mains electricity supply or an independent generator.

Supplying cold water to country-house bathrooms was only half the battle, however, a hot water supply was also needed, and that presented an entirely different set of problems. To see how those problems were resolved we must return to the technological focal point of any country house – the service range – and traditional ways of heating water.

In the eighteenth century, water for washing and bathing was heated in coppers and carried by hand to wherever it was needed. In the nineteenth century, enclosed kitchen ranges incorporating hot-water boilers or back boilers began to be introduced into country-house kitchens. They superseded the use of coppers for many tasks, but while the back boilers of kitchen-ranges could, in theory at least, have provided a piped supply, they could still only heat relatively small amounts of water. That may have been sufficient to serve a plumbed-in washbasin, or possibly a hip bath, but it would have been incapable of supplying the copious amounts of water needed for even a single, conventional Victorian bathroom.

To provide hot water for one or more plumbed-in bathrooms, a large, designated boiler was required, along with a hot-water storage cylinder. The hot water rose to the storage cylinder from the boiler on a flow and return system, based on the principle that hot water (being less dense than cold water), rises and displaces the denser, cooler water, which then returns to the boiler to be reheated.

In early installations, 'direct' storage cylinders were used, in which the hot water was simply stored in a cylinder until it was either drawn off at the tap, or it cooled and returned to the boiler. That was the system adopted at Stackpole Court in the 1830s, where there was a single bathroom on the first floor, served by a boiler on the floor below (Cawdor Archives, Box 236B, Carmarthenshire Archives Service).

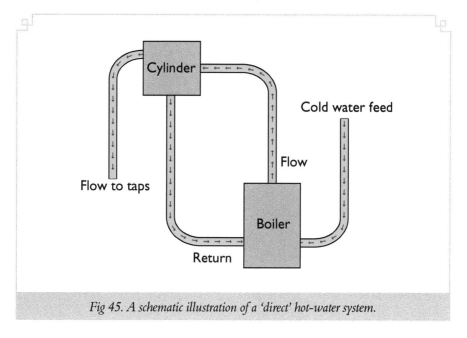

Fig 45. A schematic illustration of a 'direct' hot-water system.

One of the problems of the 'direct' storage system was that because fresh water, along with its impurities such as lime, was constantly being drawn into the boiler, it caused lime-scaling in the boiler, storage cylinder and pipe work. That problem was overcome in the late-nineteenth century with the development of 'indirect' storage cylinders, in which the hot water passed through the storage cylinder in an inner coil. The inner coil acted like a modern-day immersion heater; it heated the water in the cylinder, and it was that water that was drawn off at the taps. Because the water in the boiler, internal pipe-work, and inner coil was constantly being re-circulated, no added impurities entered the system and the problem of scaling was significantly reduced.

Even with a suitably efficient boiler, providing piped hot water to multiple bathrooms scattered throughout a large country house presented challenging logistical problems. If there were long pipe runs between the hot-water storage cylinder and individual bathrooms, the draw-off times could be tediously long, and by the time the water reached the tap, if not actually cold, it was often tepid. Getting hot water to widely dispersed bathrooms in large country houses only really became feasible with the introduction of individual water heaters. Gas-fired water geysers were available from the 1880s, but no examples of their use in country houses in the region have so far come to light – probably because so few houses had a gas supply. Back boilers linked to individual open fires in bedrooms and dressing rooms would have been the obvious solution, and though back boilers were installed extensively in newly built urban properties in the 1920s and 1930s, for some reason they were not used in country houses. Electric immersion heaters, developed in the 1920s, were the ultimate solution to the problem. They could be installed wherever required, and only needed electricity, a storage cylinder and a supply of piped cold water in order to provide sufficient hot water for a lengthy soak in a bath, virtually at the flick of a switch.

While bathrooms in country houses were seen as eminently desirable – and with improvements to the technology, entirely feasible to install – they weren't cheap. In 1900, a typical wash-hand basin cost £3, while a shower bath could cost as much as £28 (Roberts, 1997, p.90; Roberts, 2001, p.24); the equivalent respectively of about £300 and £3,000 today. That is possibly one reason why, apart from the bathroom linked to the master bedroom, bathrooms in country houses continued to be something of a rarity well into the twentieth century. The other reason was that shared bathrooms intended for use by guests or junior members of the family were not universally welcomed. The gentry were disinclined to share their bathrooms with their guests, and many visitors disliked even the thought of using a bath or water-closet that had just previously been used by another member of the household (Franklin, 1981, p.113).

Ladies in particular, preferred to wash and bathe in the privacy of their own bedrooms, rather than be seen in their dressing gowns and without makeup, trooping back and forth between their bedroom and a communal bathroom. It was slightly less of a problem in country houses where separate wings or corridors were provided for male and female guests, and where each corridor or wing had its own bathroom. However, it still didn't overcome the problem of everyone wanting to use the bathroom at the same time. The solution to that particular dilemma was for guests to 'wash' in the privacy of their own bedrooms (making use of traditional washstands and wash-basins) and to use the shared bathroom solely for 'bathing'. Conflicts about who would use the bathroom, and when, were resolved by adopting a simple, unofficial timetabling arrangement.

Plumbed-in bathrooms for servants, if provided at all, were only introduced very slowly, and out of a sense of decorum, there was generally a strict separation between those for male and female servants. Both Stackpole Court and Newton House provided bathrooms for their servants – along with a strict, gender-based and hierarchical rota for those wishing to use them.

Fig 46. The servants' bathroom at Newton House.

Even without such bathing facilities, cleanliness was expected of all domestic servants, especially those coming into contact with, or in close proximity to, the gentry.

While the relatively slow take-up of bathrooms in Welsh country houses was primarily due to logistical and financial factors, it was also significantly influenced by the fact that washing and bathing in the privacy of one's own bedroom remained such a pleasant and convenient experience.

CHAMBER POTS AND WATER CLOSETS

Chamber pots were by far the most common form of indoor sanitation in Britain in the eighteenth and nineteenth centuries. They were ubiquitous and used by all classes in society, and the Welsh gentry fully accepted them as the mainstay of domestic sanitation in their country houses. For the gentry, chamber pots had a number of advantages; they could be used in the warmth, comfort and privacy of their bedrooms, and unlike early forms of water closet, there was no mechanism to break down; they didn't need a water supply or extensive plumbing, and they were emptied and cleaned, as if by magic, discretely and unobserved by domestic servants. Furthermore, even the best quality chamber pots were relatively cheap in comparison to water closets, and when not in use they could be hidden away out of sight under the bed or in 'pot cupboards'.

The pot cupboards used in gentry households were often attractively designed pieces of furniture, with the advantage of being easily recognisable by visitors and guests – a useful attribute when staying in a strange house. Chamber pots, continued to be used by the squirearchy well into the nineteenth century and beyond. For example, in the 1874 inventory for Ffynone, they were listed in the North, West, South and East bedrooms (and also in the dressing rooms of the South and East bedrooms), as well as in the butler's bedroom, the housekeeper's bedroom and the servant girls' room (Ffynone inventory, 1874, National Library of Wales).

A slightly more sophisticated, often even luxurious, version of the chamber pot was the 'close stool', a sort of early commode. Like the pot cupboard, it was a piece of furniture designed to be on permanent display. In addition to the standard chamber pot, it had a toilet seat (sometimes padded for greater comfort) and a lid to hide the pot from view, all in the guise of a small cupboard, chair or set of bed-steps.

70

Unlike a chamber pot that generally had to be crouched over, close stools were designed as seats, giving them the added advantage of height and stability. In the best country-house bedrooms, close stools were often exquisitely-made and expensive pieces of furniture; those by Sheraton, for example, were designed so that they could stand 'in a genteel room without giving offence to the eye' and 'in a style elevated above their use' (quoted in Christie, 2000, p.259). The close stools at Stradey, for example, were made of mahogany with padded horsehair seats (Bill of Sale, 1788,

Fig 47. A close stool.

Carmarthenshire Archives Service). Because of their attractiveness and usefulness, they remained in use in country-house bedrooms well into the twentieth century. Even when they were ultimately superseded by water closets, they were rarely thrown away and instead were retained for use in sick rooms. The auction of the household goods of the late Thomas Thomas J.P. of Wellfield House in 1913 provides clear evidence of the retention of such facilities in a typical gentry house. Among the goods auctioned were: hip and sponge baths, mahogany marble-topped washstands, a mahogany commode, an armchair commode, a bedsteps commode and 'bedroom ware' [the ubiquitous chamber pots] (Carmarthen Journal and South Wales Weekly Advertiser, 23 Jan, 1913, p.4).

Unlike the commodes openly referred to in the Thomas Thomas auction of 1913, the close stools in the Stradey inventory of 1829 were more coyly referred to as night chairs, which raises the issue of changing terminology and the use of euphemisms when discussing toilet facilities. The compilers of inventories were often reluctant to use such basic terms as chamber pots when listing the contents of the principal bedrooms of gentry-houses, instead describing them as chamber ware or bedroom ware. Another common area of confusion is the term 'lavatory'. In the twenty-first century, lavatory generally means a toilet – or, at least, a room containing a toilet. In the nineteenth century, however, it simply referred to a room containing a washbasin. Similarly, the term 'maids' closet' didn't mean a WC provided for the exclusive use of maids, but rather a room containing a piped water supply and a slop sink. It was where chamber pots could be emptied and cleaned, and where brushes, mops and cleaning materials could be stored. Even in country houses without a maids' closet, chamber pots were rarely carried down the backstairs to be emptied and cleaned. Instead, housemaids with slop pails and buckets of clean water would enter the various bedrooms, empty the contents of the chamber pots into the slop pail, and then clean the chamber pots with fresh water. Only covered slop pails were carried out of the bedrooms to be emptied into the drains.

Fig 48. A slop pail at Llanerchaeron.

Chamber pots were so useful and convenient that they weren't restricted solely to the bedrooms of country houses. Most country houses set aside a cloakroom or dressing room, complete with a chamber pot or close stool, for their visitors. For obvious reasons, cloakrooms were generally located just off the entrance hall, and because architects almost invariably placed the male suite of rooms (the library, billiard room and smoking room) close to the entrance hall, the cloakroom chamber pot came to be used solely by the gentlemen of the family and their male guests. If the distance between the male suite of rooms and the cloakroom was to great, chamber pots were sometimes used in situ in the billiard or smoking room. Out of a sense of decorum, they would be used behind a screen in the corner of the room and would never have been used in mixed company. A separate dressing room would be set aside for female visitors (Evans, 2011, p.105). To ensure the chamber pots in those rooms were always in a pristine state and ready for the next user, a maid would be given the task of emptying and cleaning them whenever they had been used.

Given the comfort and convenience of chamber-pot sanitation, it is hardly surprising that owners of country houses were so reluctant to go to the trouble and expense of installing water closets, especially as there was such little advantage in doing so. In contrast to the cheap and reliable chamber pot, early water closets (valve closets) were expensive, mechanically complex, and frequently temperamental pieces of engineering. Valve closets, as the name suggests, relied on a complicated system of inter-linked valves. They were extortionately expensive and subject to malfunctioning, even so the more avant-garde of the Welsh gentry began installing water closets in the early-eighteenth century. At Picton Castle in 1729, there were water closets next to the hall, parlour, drawing room and damask room, and on the upper floors there were a further ten – one for each bedroom. The nursery and schoolroom also had a water closet (Howell, 1986, p.179). Picton Castle was, admittedly, something of a rarity at the time and it is unclear precisely what types of water closets were installed. It was not until the late-eighteenth century that advances in valve-closet design progressed sufficiently enough to make them acceptably wholesome and dependable. Alexander Cummings and Joseph Bramah, in 1775 and 1778 respectively, made and patented significant technical refinements to valve-closet design.

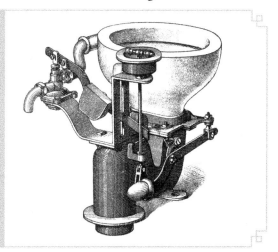

Fig 49. The improved, Bramah-type valve closet. Raising the handle next to the toilet bowl opened a valve at the base of the bowl, discharging the contents into the soil pipe. At the same time, a valve in the water cistern opened and water from the cistern acted to flush out the whole system. When the handle was lowered, both valves closed, leaving a small amount of water in the toilet bowl.

Good quality valve closets were undeniably expensive, which was possibly part of their appeal – plus the fact that royalty and the nobility were also known to favour them. Not only was the initial cost of a valve closet high, but it also needed to be installed by skilled craftsmen. The mahogany toilet seat and enclosing cabinet alone cost something in the region of three or four pounds (the equivalent of about £300 today). While there were cheaper forms of water closet on the market – such as the pan closet – these were prone to smell, malfunction and leak.

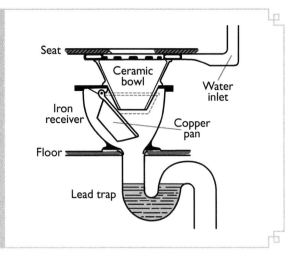

Fig 50. An example of a pan closet. When the toilet handle was lifted, instead of opening a valve, the pan beneath the bowl fell open emptying its contents into the trap below. The system was inefficient and difficult to clean thoroughly, meaning that each time the handle was raised unpleasant smells entered the room.

Although expensive, valve closets were the gentry's water closet of choice, but its installation was not embarked upon lightly. When the installation of a water closet was being considered for Stradey in the 1820s, there were lengthy and detailed discussions surrounding the practicalities of the work involved (Stradey Archives, file 1651, Carmarthenshire Archives Service). To ensure that there was an adequate water supply to that solitary water closet, a 20-foot deep well had to be sunk, and a cistern and hand pump provided (Letter, dated 17 Oct 1821, Stradey Archives, Carmarthenshire Archives Service).

Water closets, as the name implies, depended on a ready supply of water to flush the contents of the toilet bowl into the soil-pipe and house drains. That water was generally delivered from a storage cistern placed somewhere higher than the water closet it served. The cisterns were often placed in attics or in the towers that were seen as such an important architectural feature of many Victorian country houses. Although the towers were initially created for purely aesthetic reasons, they provided ideal locations for water-storage tanks (Franklin, 1981, pp.84-5).

The cisterns were filled by gravity feed, by pumping or by diverting rainwater into them from gullies and downspouts on the roof. In 1824, the two water closets at Middleton Hall were flushed with water from a cistern on the roof filled by gravity from a piped supply of spring water (Jones, 2006, p. 133). At Newton House, the cisterns were also fed by gravity, but from a supply pumped initially to storage tanks in the hills above the house, while at Golden Grove in the 1820s, a single rainwater cistern was used to supply all the various water closets in the house.

Jeffrey Wyattville, the architect of Golden Grove, created a sort of garderobe by placing the water closets above each other on three floors. They were all served by a single rainwater cistern, with the waste from each water closet discharging into a shared, external soil pipe (Cawdor muniments, Plan 42, Carmarthenshire Archives Service). Ball valves hadn't been developed when Wyattville was designing his system for Golden Grove, so he ensured that any overflow from the storage cistern was carried into the soil pipe.

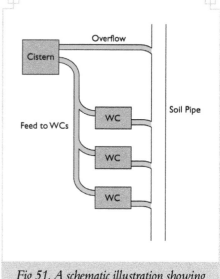

Fig 51. A schematic illustration showing the rainwater supply system at Golden Grove.

It is unclear precisely which rooms were served by the three water closets, though because of the almost pathological fear of sewer gas in the nineteenth century it is unlikely that they would have been installed in close proximity to the bedrooms. When water closets were intended to serve bedrooms, wherever possible, they were placed in a well-ventilated inner sanctum of the dressing room, totally separate from the sleeping accommodation. It was incumbent on any country landowner considering investing in new technology that while it should provide the maximum, additional convenience and prestige, it should do so without actually threatening his life, or that of his family and guests. The problem of sewer gas entering a room was to a large extent addressed by the development of the S-trap by Alexander Cummings in 1775. It required an S-shaped pipe placed horizontally between the toilet and the soil-pipe. When the toilet was flushed, enough water was retained in the bend of the pipe to act as a water seal.

Given the initial reluctance to install water closets, it is more than likely that when only one or two are mentioned in sales literature they would be in the entrance hall cloakroom and the inner sanctum of the principal dressing room – with possibly an additional one on the first floor to serve lady visitors. 'The one on the Upper Floor will then come to be considered as appropriated to ladies' (Kerr, 1864, p.170). In some country houses, water closets were also later provided on the guest wing corridors. They were deemed to be acceptably safe there because they were totally separate from the bedrooms. A water closet was installed, for example, at Stackpole Court in 1839, solely to serve the suite of 'young ladies apartments' (Plan 3, Box 236 B, Cawdor Archives, Carmarthenshire Archives Service).

A water closet near the entrance hall was seen as particularly desirable, not only because of its convenience but also because it could be found easily by visitors to the house. Robert Kerr, acknowledging, somewhat dismissively, the gentry's poor sense of direction, wrote:

> The reason for having these conveniences [water closets] connected with the Entrance is that they are provided for the use chiefly of gentlemen visitors, who can always find their way to the Entrance-Hall without trouble, if nowhere else (Kerr, 1864, p.167).

Valve closets were something of a status symbol, and when placed in cloakrooms they met three of the key demands of the gentry – comfort, convenience and prestige.

If the entrance-hall cloakroom was too far away from the male suite of rooms, an additional water closet was sometimes provided – closer to where it was needed. Lord Dynevor, for example, had three water closets installed next to the billiard and smoking room at Newton House, apparently reserving the most luxurious of the three for his personal use. The nineteenth-century move away

Fig 52. The Stradey Castle valve closet in the entrance-hall cloakroom.

from the gentry using chamber pots in company to providing conveniently located water closets reflects not only the growing reliability and prestige of water closets, but also the growing delicacy and sensibility of the squirearchy. No longer was it deemed acceptable to urinate in the same room in which others were eating, drinking or playing billiards.

As the nineteenth century progressed, and as water closets increasingly came to be seen as an essential part of civilised, country-house living, they began to be provided ever more frequently in the dressing rooms/ bathrooms of the principal bedrooms and also on the corridors of the guest wings.

Fig 53. A water closet serving one of the guest wings at Ffynone.

Even when water closets were provided to serve the bedrooms of guests and junior members of the family, chamber pots were still used in the bedrooms, especially during the night, when it was far more appealing and convenient to use a chamber pot, than to make a trip down a draughty corridor to a shared water closet. Nineteenth-century plumbing was also notoriously noisy, and using water closets in the middle of the night could destroy the sleep of the whole household. The convenience, reliability and low cost of chamber-pot sanitation goes some way to explaining the slow transition from chamber pots to water closets in Welsh country houses. When Bronwydd was refurbished in the 1850s, it had just a single water closet, and no more were added until the early-twentieth century (Baker-Jones, 2005, pp.109-110). Similarly, in 1881, Alltyrodyn had just two water closets for the whole household (Alltyrodyn sales catalogue, 1881, National Library of Wales).

It goes without saying that water closets serving the bedrooms of domestic servants were almost non-existent in Welsh country houses; instead, chamber pots continued to be used well into the twentieth century.

During the working day, domestic servants weren't expected to waste their time going to their bedrooms to use a chamber pot; instead, outdoor privy-middens close to the service range were provided. Privy-middens were built over midden pits, with the pits being emptied whenever they began to cause a nuisance.

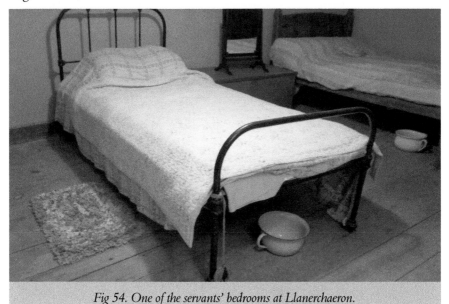

Fig 54. One of the servants' bedrooms at Llanerchaeron.

In west Wales, however, a widely adopted alternative to the privy-midden was the 'privy leat'. It was a rudimentary form of water-carriage system used extensively in the eighteenth and nineteenth centuries. It involved building the privy over a channel (leat) of continuously flowing water. As long as there was an ample supply of water, privy leats had a number of distinct advantages over the standard outdoor privy. The leats carried the urine and faeces away from the privies quickly and efficiently; the privies were virtually smell-free, never required

Fig 55. An exterior view of the privy leat at Alltyrodyn.

Fig 57. The leat serving one of the privies at Nanteos. The apertures at the top of the photograph are where the timbers supporting the toilet seat would have been positioned.

Fig 56. The interior of one of the privy leats at Llanerchaeron.

emptying and couldn't malfunction. Examples of privy leats can be found at Llanerchaeron, Nanteos, Aberglasney and Alltyrodyn.

Returning to water closets; at the start of the nineteenth century, the only water closets available were the expensive valve-type or the less salubrious pan closet. However, due to a number of significant developments in water-closet design in the 1870s and 80s, by the end of the century, cheaper and much improved water closets were available. They were the 'wash out' and the 'wash down' water closets – both were ceramic and both could incorporate an 'S' trap to prevent sewer gas entering the room. They were mass-produced in one piece, and because they were freestanding and had no mechanism to hide, they didn't need to be enclosed in a cabinet. Their smooth surfaces made them more hygienic and much easier to clean than valve-closets. The 'wash-down' design of water closet ultimately took precedence over its rival the 'wash-out' closet, largely because it had a more efficient way of flushing the bowl. It is that type of water closet that is still used in Britain today (Eveleigh, 2006, pp.115-137). The wash-down water closet was such an advance on previous designs that many country-house owners replaced their valve closets with wash-down water closets, while still keeping the mahogany seat and cabinet of the former valve closet. Doing so enabled them to enjoy all the advantages of a wash-down closet, while retaining the impressive appearance of a valve closet, along with its aura of luxury and splendour.

Although ceramic water closets were used by the gentry, cheaper and more robust glazed earthenware water closets tended to be installed in the service range, if they were installed at all. At Nanteos, for example, wash-down water closets for use by the indoor domestic servants were provided soon after they were first developed. Other country-house owners slowly followed suit, so that by the end of the century water closets for servants were becoming ever more common.

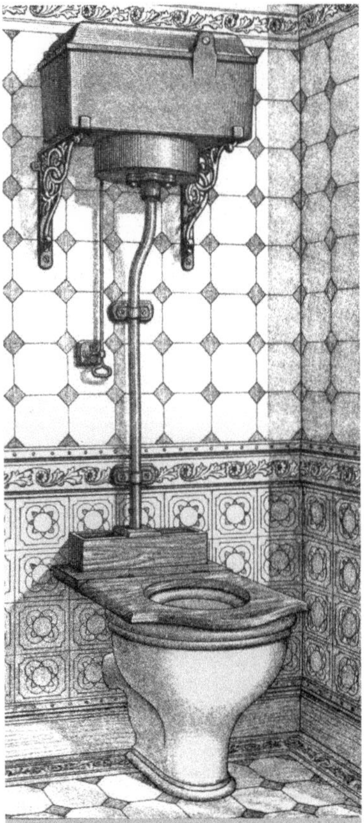

The wash-down closet was only really made practicable following the introduction of toilet cisterns with ball valves and siphonic flushing mechanisms in the second half of the nineteenth century (Eveleigh, 2006, pp.148-50). That was because the mechanism in the cistern was simple, and because it delivered several gallons of water quickly and with concentrated force.

The wash-down water closet and the siphonic flushing cistern were such an improvement on previous water closet

Fig 58. An advertisement for a wash-down water closets, complete with waste-water preventing cisterns, c.1881.

designs that by the end of the century hardly any country house in Wales was without at least one water closet. They were seen as a prestigious addition to the house, and the precise number of water closets figured prominently in country-house sales literature.

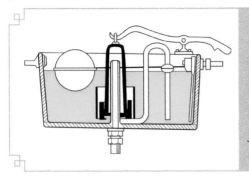

Fig 59. A schematic illustration of a siphonic flushing cistern and ball-valve. The floating ball, attached by an arm to the ball-valve, cuts off the flow of water when the water in the cistern has reached the required level. The siphon uses atmospheric pressure to force water into the flushing pipe when the 'bell' is raised.

However, the growing number of water closets, baths and wash hand basins in country houses inevitably led to an additional burden on the 'traditional' methods of disposing of liquid waste – that is discharging it into nearby streams and rivers. Writing in 1912, Alban Scott stated:

> It is only during the last few years that this important subject [sewage disposal] has been seriously considered generally by property-owners. It has usually been sufficient for them to hope that all was well so long as the house itself was not apparently inconvenienced (Scott, quoted in Weaver, 1912, p.84).

Drainage had always been seen as an important consideration when planning the design and location of country houses. Large houses with extensive roofs had to dispose of colossal amounts of rainwater, which needed to be channelled away from the house quickly and efficiently, along with the liquid waste from the kitchen, laundry and stable block.

In a typical, eighteenth-century country house, faecal matter from chamber pots and close stools was just dumped onto midden heaps for use by the home farm as manure. Urine from the household's chamber pots, along with other forms of liquid waste and water from rainwater downspouts, was simply channelled into the house-drains and discharged into the nearest watercourse. To drain a large country house efficiently, an extensive and sophisticated network of house drains was required, and large open areas, such as stable yards, were cobbled and gradients provided to channel any surface water into central drains and to be carried away.

Even though important, the subject of drainage may still not have been an all-consuming passion for the Welsh gentry in the eighteenth century. However, the subject grew in importance during the nineteenth century, largely due to the link being made between diseases such as cholera and faulty drainage. In 1855, for example, the sale catalogue for Hafod boasted:

> The drainage, both ground and surface has been most particularly attended to; and is conveyed in glazed stoneware pipes, to a new main sewer, five feet high, and extending direct from the mansion to the river (Hafod sales catalogue, 1855).

In a slightly later sale catalogue for Hafod (1864), the main sewer was described as being flushed continuously by a brook running through it. Flushing the sewer in that way would have helped prevent any build-up of solids and would therefore have reduced the risk of sewer gas entering the house. Discharging sewage into nearby water courses was the normal, widely adopted means of disposal throughout the nineteenth century, and even with the growing number of water closets in a typical country house, discharging sewage into the streams and rivers running through a country estate would not have presented a significant environmental problem. Only the contents of a relatively small number of water closets, diluted by rainwater and the waste water from baths and washbasins, would have entered the watercourses, and would have been further diluted by the streams and rivers themselves. The drains at Alltyrodyn, for example, discharged into an open channel in the ha-ha at the front of the house, which ultimately fed into a nearby river. The channel was periodically flushed by releasing water into it from a nearby fishpond.

Although there were undoubtedly health implications if contaminated sewage entered a water course that was subsequently used for drinking water, it wasn't until the closing years of the nineteenth century that British towns and cities began to treat their much more heavily polluted sewage before discharging it into the rivers running through them. And it was only after an Act of Parliament in 1888 that river pollution by urban authorities began to be seriously addressed. Only much later did the focus shift to the pollution caused by remote and isolated country estates.

Very few country-house owners felt the need to divert water-closet waste from the watercourses running through their estates. Those who did, generally did so by arranging for the foul-water drains to discharge into cesspools, which were emptied periodically and the contents used as manure. Cesspools were underground chambers lined with stone or brick, which, in theory at least, prevented the contents leaking into the surrounding subsoil. In the late-nineteenth century, as landowners were increasingly discouraged from discharging raw sewage into the nation's rivers, septic tanks and soakaways began to be used. A septic tank acted like a more technically sophisticated form of cesspool; it was watertight and fully enclosed. The liquid waste from the house was piped into the septic tank, and by anaerobic action – using bacteria that thrive in the absence of oxygen – the organic solids were digested and reduced, often by as much as 85 per cent. The effluent from the septic tank was then passed into a soakaway pit filled with rubble, which allowed the waste water to seep into the surrounding subsoil. Cesspools, septic tanks and soakaways were built far enough away from the house to ensure that any smell from them did not cause a nuisance to the house or pleasure gardens.

In towns and cities, percolating filter beds began to be used extensively in the twentieth century to treat sewage before discharging it into nearby rivers. In a percolating filter bed, liquid sewage was sprayed from rotating arms onto the rough aggregate making up the filter bed. The arms were driven by the force of the liquid entering the pipe work, rather like a modern-day lawn sprinkler. The liquid sewage 'percolated' slowly through the filter bed and was digested and purified by aerobic action, that is by bacteria in the filter

Fig 60. The percolating filter bed at Falcondale, built in the twentieth century.

bed that thrive on an abundance of oxygen. The effluent from the filter beds was then passed either into a soakaway or a convenient watercourse. Such systems were more expensive to provide than septic tanks and needed more maintenance, and so were rarely adopted on Welsh country estates. However, Falcondale was one of the few country houses that did adopt such a system. At each stage in the sanitary evolution of country-houses, the comfort and convenience of members of the family remained paramount. As long as there were servants to clean and empty chamber pots, they were the preferred option for bedroom use, largely because of their cheapness, convenience and reliability. It was only when water closets began to be seen as something of a status symbol, and when most of the technical problems associated with them had been overcome, that they were introduced extensively in Welsh country houses. Not only did water closets come to be seen as more decorous to use than chamber pots, but in the twentieth century, with a declining number of servants to clean and empty them, chamber pots began to go out of fashion and water closets became a necessary and essential part of country house living.

Heating and Lighting

For the gentry, size really did matter. Wealth, status and prestige were intimately associated with their country houses. A large house with an imposing façade and a grand entrance hall, leading to spacious, elegantly decorated and well-furnished reception rooms provided a tangible indication of a family's elite position in society. However, the larger the house and the more numerous the rooms, the more difficult and expensive it was to heat and light adequately. To live stylishly, entertain lavishly, and to enjoy all the indoor pastimes and pursuits available to the wealthy, a country house needed to be well lit and comfortably warm. The gentry, therefore, used a combination of servants and technology to ensure they could enjoy life to the full, whatever the time of day or the season of the year.

One way of keeping warm, of course, was to dress appropriately, and the gentry could afford to clothe themselves in multiple layers of cotton, wool and silk. Although fashion and occasion may sometimes have required the ladies to wear unseasonably light, flimsy or revealing clothing, on the whole, the gentry dressed for warmth – if not always for comfort.

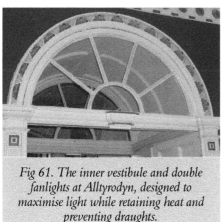

Fig 61. The inner vestibule and double fanlights at Alltyrodyn, designed to maximise light while retaining heat and preventing draughts.

Another obvious way of staying warm indoors was to reduce draughts and keep the cold air out. That was notoriously difficult in large, rambling, uninsulated houses, but was achieved to a limited extent by using internal window shutters, heavy curtains, wing-backed chairs and inglenook fireplaces. Vestibules were also used as rudimentary airlocks, to reduce the amount of warm air escaping and cold air entering a house whenever the front door was opened.

Heavy drapes on four-poster beds also helped reduce the draughts that were inevitable in large, high-ceilinged bedrooms with poorly fitting windows and doors.

At a more fundamental level, orientation was also seen as important. In the eighteenth and nineteenth centuries, architects skilfully employed orientation not only to provide impressive vistas, but also to make maximum use of sun and shade to heat or cool specific rooms. Accordingly, south and south-west facing rooms were used for breakfast and drawing rooms, while the cooler north-facing rooms were used as dining rooms, kitchens and pantries.

For real warmth and comfort in the depths of winter however, additional artificial heating was needed. Open fires were the traditional and most widespread way of heating country houses, with virtually every room boasting at least one fireplace. Fireplaces varied dramatically in size and ornamentation, from the huge log fires in the principal reception rooms, to the smaller coal fires in bedrooms and dressing rooms. In the main hall and the drawing room, fireplaces were deliberately designed to impress. They were characteristically large, and often lavish and ornate. They served a dual purpose: to warm the room and to demonstrate the owner's wealth, prestige and hospitality.

Although much of the heat from the fire was wasted as it went straight up the chimney, open fires were still preferred to the more efficient, continental stoves that became available in the nineteenth century. Open fires radiated heat and hospitality, and most country landowners could draw on their estate's forests and woodlands for fuel. Some, such as the Mansels of Stradey Castle, also had access to coal from their own coalmines. Even so, the amount of fuel needed to heat a large country house was substantial.

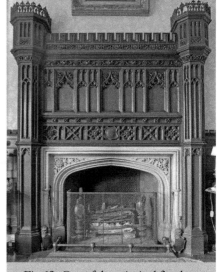

Fig 62. One of the principal fireplaces at Stradey Castle.

In the late-eighteenth century, for example, it took sixty-four wagon loads of coal a year to heat Golden Grove (Cawdor Muniments, 26/2259, 27 Sept 1788, Carmarthenshire Archives Service).

Traditionally, coal was delivered by sea to coastal ports before being moved to its final destination by road. That presented particular logistical problems, due to its weight, its bulk and the abysmal state of the roads – one possible reason why the Welsh gentry were so heavily involved in the creation of turnpike trusts. With the development of the railway network in the second half of the nineteenth century, coal was increasingly carried by rail to inland depots, which made transporting it to its final destination significantly easier. Nanteos, for example, got its supplies from the railway station at Aberystwyth (letter dated 15th Dec 1909, National Library of Wales). Once delivered, it still had to be stored somewhere dry – either in a coal cellar or coal store near the service range. At Nanteos, an ingenious system was devised to move the coal from the coal storage yard to the service-range coal store; a short railway track was built between the two, with a buffer at the end of the track. The coal trucks were run down the track by hand; then, when they hit the buffer, they would upend and shoot the coal into the yard below. The coal, along with logs, was stored in a separate building to keep it dry until needed. As in the case of other country houses, the coal was carried into the house by one of the servants – generally, the 'odd man'.

It should be noted that wood and coal were not interchangeable fuels. Open fires were designed to burn either logs or coal, but not both. Log fires used firedogs (andirons), whereas coal fires needed a raised metal basket to burn most efficiently.

The difference relates to air flow; coal needs a flow of air under the bed of fuel, while logs burn best lying in their own ashes, but leant against the

Fig 63. Firedogs © National Trust.

horizontal bars of the firedogs. Because coal was a more efficient fuel than timber, fireplaces designed to burn coal could be reduced in size. This also increased the draw of the chimney, making the fire burn even better. The usual practice was to have coal fires in bedrooms and log fires in the principal reception rooms. A roaring log fire, set in a large, impressive fireplace was hard to match in terms of providing a warm, congenial welcome. In the late-nineteenth century, however, in an attempt to improve the efficiency of fires in the principal rooms, the cavernously large fireplace openings were reduced in size, and dog grates able to burn coal were inserted. It was a common practice to

Fig 64. Coal grate © National Trust/ Sue James.

design the dog grates so that they could be attached, when required, to the existing firedogs, thus providing the option of the best of both worlds.

In a well-run household, fires would be lit so that rooms would already be warm when members of the family entered them. With ample servants to tend fires and to carry coal and logs throughout the house, there was little incentive to install central heating. Unfortunately, one of the problems of only heating rooms actually in use or about to be used was that the corridors and staircases leading to them remained unheated. If the corridors weren't actually cold, they were invariably chilly, and added to the potential for draughts. To overcome that problem, in the nineteenth century a number of wealthy families began to install partial central heating in corridors, lobbies and entrance halls. In 1841, for example, a partial central heating system was installed at Stackpole Court to 'warm the corridors [and] passages to the visitors' bedrooms and the young ladies' apartments, and the back stairs' (Letters, dated Jan 1841 and July 1841, Box 236 A, Cawdor Archives, Carmarthenshire Archives Service).

Stackpole Court was possibly at the fore in installing central heating, partial or otherwise, in the 1840s. More typical was Stradey Castle, which did not include any form of central heating when it was built in the 1850s, but installed partial central heating during major expansion work in the 1870s. At that time, it was provided in the vestibule, hall and corridors (though not on the nursery landing). The radiators were encased in large ornate, marble-topped radiator covers. The system used a coal-fired boiler and large-bore cast-iron heating pipes. It was only when the original boiler was replaced by another coal-fired boiler in 1936 that central heating was finally extended to the nursery landing (Stradey Archives, Box 27, MS. 2110, Carmarthenshire Archives Service). Coal was the logical choice of fuel for Stradey Castle because of the Mansell's mining interests (Stradey Archives, MS 1637, Carmarthenshire Archives Service), but it was also the most commonly used fuel for central heating boilers across Wales – as improved transport links by the late nineteenth century made it more easily accessible.

Early central heating systems relied on convection, rather than pumps, to circulate the hot water. That placed severe restrictions on the number of radiators that could be included in the system, and on their location, as the pipe runs had to rise and fall uninterruptedly or the circulation would be impaired. Circulation, in any case, was slow, and the heat from the radiators on the return leg was significantly reduced. Those twin problems were only resolved with the introduction of electric circulating pumps in the early-twentieth century. Before that, the larger and more rambling the house, the more inefficient the system became, which goes some way to explain the often limited central heating systems initially installed in many country houses. Furthermore, a significant number of country landowners deliberately chose not to introduce any form of central heating in their homes. It was, for example, never installed at Nanteos or Llanerchaeron. The reluctance to provide central heating was not based solely on logistical problems or considerations of cost, but on the widely held belief that central heating was unhealthy, if not actually effete (Musson, 2009, p.241). Even in the 1920s, many people felt that radiators in bedrooms were harmful to one's health, and that bedrooms were better kept either cool, or heated only by open fires which at least helped to improve ventilation (Aslet, 1982, p.111).

Although there was, undeniably, some initial reluctance to provide central heating, once partial central heating had been installed, the next logical step was to extend it further and provide radiators in all the principal reception rooms. Such installations supplemented the open fires and helped to reduce draughts. However, even with a rudimentary central heating system and fireplaces in every room, many country houses could still be uncomfortably chilly in the depths of winter. Furthermore, it wasn't always convenient or practical to light fires in rooms that would only be used temporarily. Something of a solution to the problem emerged in the late-nineteenth century with the development of freestanding paraffin stoves, though their smell prevented them from being used extensively in country houses. A more acceptable and much more widely adopted way of heating rooms used only briefly or occasionally, was the electric fire. While they would rarely have been used in the principal rooms of the house, and certainly never when entertaining guests, they were a convenient way of heating other rooms, especially bedrooms.

Central heating in Welsh country houses remained something of a rarity throughout the nineteenth century, but it grew in popularity in the early-twentieth century when central heating and piped hot water supplies came to be seen as the norm. Writing in 1911, the architect, Robert Briggs, stated:

> …in larger Houses, additional heating should be provided by hot water and radiators with a separate boiler. There is also economy in this arrangement, as the kitchen range can be used only for the cooking, and the hot water for the Baths, Pantry and Scullery will be supplied from the separate boiler. There should, for the purposes of economy, be two boilers: one for the radiators, used only in cold weather, and the other for the hot water, used of course all the year round (Briggs, 1911, p.61).

Welsh landowners previously opposed to installing central heating in their homes, finally capitulated. Sir Marteine Lloyd of Bronwydd installed central heating (at a cost of almost £300) in the early-twentieth century (Baker-Jones, 2005, p.110), as did the owners of Alltyrodyn Mansion, where a small, coal-fired boiler was placed just below the level of the service-range corridor. The Alltyrodyn system used a combination of cast-iron pipes and large coiled radiators to heat the house, but it is unlikely that it would ever have been capable of providing anything other than background heat. Placing the boiler in the service-range corridor suggests that the system was intended to be monitored and stoked by indoor domestic staff, whereas most country-house boilers were the responsibility of either the odd-job man or one of the under-gardeners. Gardeners were preferred because of their familiarity with the boilers and heating systems used in the stove houses of kitchen gardens.

In the depths of winter, it took huge amounts of coal to feed the voracious appetites of country-house boilers. Depending on the size of the house, the boiler needed to be stoked at least three or four times a day, which posed something of a logistical problem in moving coal to the boiler room. In most installations, that problem was overcome by dumping the coal in bulk into a cellar near the boiler room or, as at Ffynone, into the boiler room itself.

On very cold days, even with the boiler working at full capacity, without the widespread us of open fires, early central-heating systems would rarely have been able to heat the whole house adequately. Spacious, high-ceilinged rooms with large, single-glazed windows and poor draught proofing didn't lend themselves to a warm, cosy, country-house experience. As a consequence, along with a broad acceptance that at times some parts of the house would almost always be cool, if not actually cold, traditional open fires continued to provide the bulk of the day-to-day heating requirements. The flexibility of only heating rooms in actual use ensured the retention of open fires well into the twentieth century.

In the inter-war period, however, there was a noticeable change in social perceptions and aspirations regarding the ideal ambient temperature of country houses. The relatively Spartan approach to domestic heating of earlier generations was abandoned and replaced by a desire for greater warmth and convenience. Unfortunately, that change in attitude coincided with a period of rising taxation and deteriorating income from land. It also coincided with increasing difficulties in recruiting and retaining domestic staff willing to undertake the arduous duties of tending open fires. Many landowners simply couldn't afford the cost of installing or running modern central heating systems capable of heating large, multi-roomed, multi-storied houses. Instead, they were forced to close up significant parts of the house and retreat into fewer rooms, only making use of their inefficient, archaic central heating systems on special occasions. In practice, most of the gentry relied on a combination of coal fires and electric heaters.

The advantages of electric fires, especially in bedrooms, were obvious. They were clean, labour-free and provided almost instantaneous heat. They were also convenient and flexible to use. Unfortunately, even in the inter-war years, many country houses still did not have an electricity supply capable of meeting the demands of multiple electric fires.

LIGHTING

We live in an age in which it is taken for granted that, whatever the time of day or the season of the year, there will always be sufficient indoor lighting to do what we like, when we want to do it. However, that was not always the case, and it is now hard to fully appreciate the inconvenience and limitations of long winter evenings spent in gloomily lit country houses. Even in the houses of the gentry, for much of the period 1750-1930, candles and oil lamps were used only sparingly because of their expense, and gas lighting, introduced in towns and cities in the late-eighteenth century, was rarely installed in country houses. Electric lighting, first developed in the 1880s, was much more frequently installed, but unless provided by the country-house owners themselves, even that wasn't available in isolated rural areas. It was not until well after 1933 and the creation of the Central Electricity Board (later nationalised in 1947 to form the National Grid) that mains electricity began to be truly accessible to the majority of country-house owners.

Prior to that, making the most of any natural light was an important element in country-house design. Throughout the eighteenth and nineteenth centuries, the architecture and orientation of country houses was manipulated to increase the amount of natural light entering rooms. Large windows in the principal reception rooms not only provided views over the pleasure gardens and rolling parkland, but also flooded those rooms with light. Bay windows and fanlights also increased the amount of daylight available, while top-lit entrance halls and lantern windows on stairwells and landings were other architectural gambits frequently adopted. Golden Grove, Llanerchaeron and Stradey Castle all used such devices to increase their natural light levels.

Fig 65. The top-lit hall at Stradey Castle.

During daylight hours, top-lit stairwells made entrance halls and staircases much lighter and airier than they could otherwise possibly have been. Another way of gaining the maximum amount of natural daylight was to create 'light wells' by building houses round a central courtyard (as at Stackpole

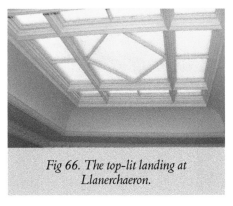

Fig 66. The top-lit landing at Llanerchaeron.

Court). The rooms and corridors looking out onto the courtyard thereby benefited from the natural daylight provided. Stackpole Court also used skylights and dormer windows to increase the amount of natural light to the upper floors of the main house and to the service range. Frosted windows in the service range were also used to gain as much 'borrowed' light as possible from the service stairwell.

Bronwydd provides an excellent example of an architect's skill in providing ample natural light in a challenging design concept. Bronwydd, though built in the 1850s, had all the appearance of a medieval manor house (Baker-Jones, 2005, p.102), but apart from the dining room, which fashion decreed should not be in direct sunlight, the rest of the house was light and airy, with numerous windows and ample natural light (Bennett Morgan, 1984, p.396).

Bronwydd was built soon after the government had abandoned the widely despised window tax (imposed between 1696 and 1851). When the

Fig 67. Bronwydd.

tax was first introduced, there was an annual, flat-rate tax of two shillings per house, plus an additional variable rate based on the total number of windows. Houses with more than twenty windows were charged eight shillings per year (the equivalent today of about £50). Most country houses easily exceeded the twenty-window rate, so a few more windows here or there would hardly have been significant, though the tax was undoubtedly an irritant. In 1789, for example, the annual window tax for Golden Grove was £10.11s (Cawdor Archives 27/2409, Carmarthenshire Archives Service), the equivalent of about £1,500 today. The window tax was difficult to evade because tax assessors could gauge the number of windows without ever needing to enter the house in question. Robert Kerr, a Victorian architect, writing in the 1860s, certainly applauded the repeal of the tax saying:

> Since the abolition of that ill-contrived impost the Window duty, which made it necessary for the designer of even a Gentleman's House to reduce its light to the verge of darkness, and its freshness to an equal extremity of denial, the number of windows, more especially in the Offices and Thoroughfares (where, indeed, they are most wanted), has very much increased; and, accordingly, both light and ventilation have been much improved (Kerr, 1864, p.86)

Though most landowners would have begrudged paying the window tax, it may not have seriously deterred them from having the precise number of windows they wanted. It may even have encouraged some to have more windows than was absolutely necessary. The ostentatiously lavish use of windows on the main facades of a country house provided a visible demonstration of the owner's wealth, elegance and style, and as they could be seen from afar, were an obvious status symbol.

Although the number, size, and location of windows determined the overall amount of natural light entering a room, the internal décor and fittings could also be used to enhance those light levels. White or near-white ceilings and walls obviously helped, as did large mirrors and polished silver fittings by reflecting any available natural or artificial light. Admittedly, the Victorian fondness for heavy, sombre, wall coverings, gloomy drapes and dark furniture seems to go against that approach somewhat, but fashion can sometimes dictate convenience.

Natural light, by definition, is restricted to daylight hours, so, when all else failed, households had to resort to artificial lighting. In the eighteenth century, that consisted primarily of candles and oil lamps. Good quality beeswax candles were expensive and required regular attention, and it is something of a myth that huge chandeliers and candelabras were commonplace and used extensively in country houses. In reality, they were reserved for a few principal rooms, special occasions and celebrations. Not only were beeswax candles expensive, but they were also taxed in the eighteenth and nineteenth centuries. Given the expense of beeswax candles, under normal circumstances, every effort was made to restrict the number in use and to gain as much light as possible from the ones used. To reflect the light that was so costly to produce, wall sconces for candles often incorporated mirrors or highly polished, reflective surfaces. The crystal glass droplets of chandeliers and candelabras also helped to radiate the candlelight. The impact of chandeliers and candelabras when ablaze with candles was spectacular and breathtaking, and a display of luxury and extravagance that was hard to match.

For obvious reasons, moveable objects such as candlesticks rarely survive in their original locations, but inventories provide an invaluable, contemporaneous

Fig 68. One of the chandeliers at Ffynone, which is lit solely by candles.

insight into where specific objects such as candlesticks were located and, by implication, how people actually lived their lives at specific points in time. The early-nineteenth century inventories for Stradey, for example, list numerous candlesticks in its bedrooms, but none in the drawing room, dining room or breakfast parlour, suggesting that in those rooms, at least, the bulk of the light fittings were permanent fixtures – that is chandeliers and wall sconces. Although electricity was installed in Stradey Castle possibly as early as 1890, the inventory for that year still lists candlesticks in all the main bedrooms – evidence, perhaps, that electric lighting did not extend to the bedrooms at that time, or that the supply was intermittent or temperamental. It is more than likely, however, that in most gentry houses people retired to bed with a single candle, and the final act of the day was to snuff out their candle.

Oil lamps were safer and more convenient than candles because they were less likely to be knocked over or blown out by a draught. They could also burn for longer if left unattended. Unfortunately, early-eighteenth-century oil lamps were poorly designed, inefficient and smelly. They used fish or whale oil, which created an unpleasant odour, and because they were heavy oils, they relied on gravity to feed the wick. That meant the oil-reservoir had to be higher than the flame and therefore cast a shadow. Because of the smell of burning whale oil, if nothing else, they tended to be used primarily in service wings and stables, rather than in the principal rooms of country houses.

Fortunately, technical developments in oil lamp design and advances in the types of oil used, changed that picture dramatically towards the end of the century. The first significant step forward was the development of

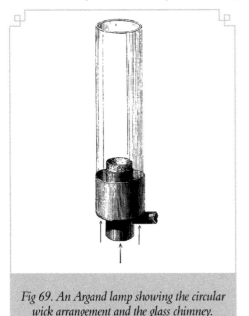

Fig 69. An Argand lamp showing the circular wick arrangement and the glass chimney.

Fig 70. An Argand oil lamp showing the oil reservoir raised above the wick.

the Argand burner in 1784. The Argand burner improved combustion because it used a circular wick and a glass chimney to increase the draught. Both the inside and outside of the wick were exposed to the air, and, in conjunction with the glass chimney the result was a much brighter and more controllable light, with far less smoke and smell.

The main drawback of the Argand lamp was that it still used a heavy oil to feed the wick, so the reservoir continued to be higher than the flame it served and therefore still cast a shadow. In the case of wall lamps, that problem was overcome by making the reservoir form part of the hanging plate. Similarly, multi-branched oil lamps were made with a central reservoir so that no shadow was cast at all, while table lamps could be placed in the corners of rooms so that the shadow of the reservoir fell into the corner, rather than into the room itself.

Although the smell of fish and whale oil continued to be something of a deterrent, the use of the more expensive sperm whale oil and colza oil (extracted from rapeseed) eased that problem somewhat, while simultaneously providing a much brighter light. Colza oil lamps began to replace whale-oil lamps in the 1820s and began to be widely used – even in the family rooms of country houses. In the Stradey inventory of 1829, two oil lamps are listed in Miss C, Lewis's bedroom, and these would almost certainly have been colza-oil lamps.

The big breakthrough in oil-lamp technology came in the mid-nineteenth century when paraffin, produced by refining mineral oil (petroleum), came into use. Paraffin oil was light enough to travel up a wick by capillary action. The reservoir could then be placed in the base of the lamp, which meant that the lamp no longer cast a shadow, and because the bulk of the lamp's weight was in its base, it was far more stable than previous lamps. Paraffin transformed the design of oil lamps and, combined with the Argand principles, led to the widespread and growing popularity of paraffin oil lamps in country houses.

By the end of the nineteenth century, country houses could be lit pleasantly, safely and adequately using a combination of oil lamps and good-quality beeswax candles. Furthermore, with the introduction of the safety match in the second half of the century, lighting candles and oil lamps became a much simpler and more convenient process. Prior to that, the only way to light a candle or oil lamp was by a taper from another flame, or by a tinderbox. Tinderboxes were notoriously time-consuming and difficult to use, especially at night in a darkened bedroom. Because of these various technical advances, most country houses in Wales continued to use candles and oil lamps even after the development of gas lighting. In fact, partly because of the expense of providing an independent gas supply and partly because of its other drawbacks, gas lighting was hardly ever installed in Welsh country houses.

Gas lighting was developed towards the end of the eighteenth century. It used coal gas made by baking coal in an oven (retort) and was initially used primarily in mills and factories, and for lighting the streets of towns and cities. In its earliest incarnation, it was dirty and smelly in operation – and almost suffocating in confined spaces. Subsequent technical developments overcame many of those early problems and coal gas became increasingly popular for lighting town houses, theatres, licensed premises, and civic building. The gas was provided by urban local authorities or private companies, neither of which was interested in supplying remote country houses. If the Welsh gentry wanted gas lighting, they had to provide it for themselves. In order to do so, a retort, a gas holder and purifiers (to remove the tar and acids in the gas) were needed – all of which required a substantial investment in terms of money and resources.

Fig 71. A typical coal-gas installation from around 1845,
designed for use in country houses.

Apart from the initial expense and disruption caused by installing gas lighting, there were other factors deterring country-house owners from doing so. Gas lighting was still widely associated with bleak urban streetscapes and grim industrial premises, and ladies found it harsh and less flattering than candlelight. Furthermore, the acids in coal gas could damage the books, paintings and interior décor of country houses. The final deterrent was that gas lights were fixed and immovable, whereas candles and candelabras could be carried between rooms, between floors and along corridors. Candles and oil lamps could also be positioned at the precise point in a room to provide the best light for specific tasks. More than anything, though, the deciding factor tipping the balance towards candlelight as opposed to gaslight was that when used lavishly, candlelight was unsurpassed in being able to provide an, exciting and exhilarating ambience to any party, ball or dinner. Such ostentatious luxury, comfort, convenience and style meant that coal-gas lighting was rarely introduced into Welsh country houses – though it was admittedly installed at Stackpole Court.

Acetylene gas was a significantly cheaper and technically simpler alternative to coal gas for lighting country houses. It was developed in the 1890s and didn't require the usual paraphernalia of coal-gas production (Hird, in Weaver, 1912, p.121).

Acetylene gas was produced by dripping water onto blocks of calcium carbide in a sealed container called a 'producer'. The gas from the producer was fed into a gasholder, which when full, tripped a valve preventing

Fig 72. An acetylene gas plant.

more water entering. As the gas was used, the gasholder sank, tripping the valve and allowing more water to enter the producer to restart the process. Calcium carbide was manufactured commercially by fusing lime and carbon together in a furnace. Acetylene gas could be used without a mantle and though providing a very clear, white light could be used in light fittings to give the appearance of candlelight. It was therefore well-suited to 'traditional' light fittings and décor (Hird, in Weaver, 1912, pp.121-2). Cilwendeg was one of the few houses in the region to be lit by acetylene gas. The system was installed in about 1920 and the gas plant (manufactured by Spensers Ltd of London) was housed in the former laundry building, close to the house. Although acetylene gas producers were small, cheap and efficient, they had already been overtaken by electric lighting by the time the technology had been fully developed. Indeed, electric lighting was, from the very start, seen as the lighting of the future.

From its development as a viable form of lighting in the 1880s, electric lighting was viewed as preferable to gas lighting, and for most day-to-day uses preferable even to candles and oil lamps. As a result, many country-house owners simply changed directly from oil lamps and candles to electric lighting. Although expensive to install, the basic principles and technology needed to provide electric lighting were relatively straightforward. All that was needed was a source of power to drive a dynamo, and the necessary wiring and electrical fittings to provide the lighting. Due to the heavy rainfall and hilly topography of west Wales, most dynamos in the region were driven by water turbines and almost all were designed to generate direct current (DC) electricity. Direct current was ideal for country-house installations, because the primary use of electricity was for lighting – normally for just a few hours in the evening. Direct current electricity could be stored in banks of batteries, which could be charged during the day ready for use in the evening.

Without being able to store electricity, the dynamo would have needed to be run whenever there was any likelihood that electricity might be required, and that would have been extremely wasteful. As long as only electric lighting was needed, it was easy to gauge demand based on the time of day, the season of the year, etc. The dynamo could then be run just long enough to keep the banks of batteries charged up. Only direct current could be stored in that way; alternating current (AC), which could be transmitted more economically over longer distances and was therefore more suited to urban use (and the national grid), could not be stored in batteries and therfore needed to be generated almost constantly.

Although water turbines, gas, petrol and steam engines could all have been used to provide the motive power to drive generators, water power had several distinct advantages over other forms of power. Water turbines were able to provide an almost instant source of power – it simply required opening an inlet valve, whereas a steam engine could operate only when a sufficient head of steam had been raised in the boiler. Furthermore, steam, gas and petrol engines all required a fairly high level of expertise to operate them efficiently, whereas a water turbine was simple to operate, reliable and almost cost-free to run. Hydroelectric systems were in any case the obvious first choice in west Wales. The ample rainfall and hilly nature of the region made water power ideally suited to generating electricity, and by the late-nineteenth century, hydraulic engineering was a well-established profession, capable of powering mills and factories, running a complex canal system, and providing domestic water supplies to towns and cities across the country. Those engineering skills were easily transferable to country-house hydroelectric schemes, which primarily involved impounding a relatively small body of water, before channelling it to a water turbine connected to a generator.

Fig 73. Stradey Castle – inlet from the holding tank to the water turbine.

The Welsh gentry adopted electric lighting with enthusiasm. They could see the obvious benefits and advantages of a clean, bright, modern form of lighting, operated by a simple flick of a switch. Stradey Castle was one of the first country houses in Wales to be lit by electricity; it was installed in the 1880s, shortly after the development of the incandescent electric light bulb in 1879. The Stradey Castle installation used a water turbine linked by belt-drive to a dynamo. The turbine replaced the waterwheel previously used to drive the estate's sawmill. Water for the turbine was carried by a headrace from a weir on the Avon Dulais, to a holding pond above the old

Fig 74. The Stradey Castle water turbine.

Fig 75. The belt-drive wheel at Stradey Castle. When connected to the dynamo (no longer present), it generated DC electricity.

sawmill. The holding pond provided a head of water and an additional level of continuity of supply, over and above that provided by the weir.

The turbine was controlled by a sluice valve in the turbine house, which when opened allowed water to enter the turbine to turn the blades and drive the dynamo.

A broadly similar system was adopted at Llanerchaeron in the early twentieth century, though in the case of Llanerchaeron the waterwheel and line-shafting previously used to drive machinery in the carpenter's workshop was used to drive the dynamo.

Fig 76. The water wheel and line-shafting at Llanerchaeron.

More typical of systems adopted in Welsh country houses in the early twentieth century, is the one installed at Clynfyw Mansion in the 1920s. At Clynfyw, water for the turbine was carried in a headrace from a millpond formed by a weir across one of the streams on the estate.

The Clynfyw system provided electric lighting for ten bedrooms, and was maintained and run by the garden staff. As well as impounding water for the turbine, the millpond at Clynfyw also served as a boating lake.

Hydroelectric schemes were, obviously, dependant on there being a suitable water supply. In the absence of water power, another way of generating electricity was by using petrol or diesel engines. They were relatively cheap in terms of initial cost; they could be placed in any outbuilding reasonably close to the main house; and they didn't require extensive hydraulic engineering work. At Nanteos, a petrol engine driving a DC dynamo was installed in 1915. The engine, dynamo and banks of batteries were all housed in a single building close to the service range, and the 100-volt supply was able to meet the demands of over forty light fittings, as well as providing power to a small number of power points. The total cost of the installation was £272, the equivalent of approximately £28,000 today.

Fig 77. The Clynfyw hydroelectric installation showing the dynamo and (bottom left) part of the water turbine. The dynamo and turbine were close coupled; that is, they were linked directly together (without a belt drive).

The most widely used petrol engines in Britain were those manufactured by the Lister Company of Dursley, Gloucester. The Lister Company also made diesel engines capable of meeting the electrical requirements of even the largest establishment. In addition, the company manufactured dynamos and electrical switchgear, all aimed deliberately at the country-house market. The system installed at Aberglasney in the 1930s, for

Fig 78. The Clynfyw boating lake.

example, was fairly typical for the period. The DC dynamo was driven by a Lister diesel engine and charged batteries in the battery house next to the generating room.

Because a reasonable knowledge of the workings of petrol and diesel engines was an advantage, the operation and maintenance of the engine and dynamo was generally undertaken by the chauffeur, if one was employed.

Gas engines were also occasionally used to generate electricity, and both Golden Grove and Newton House used gas engines. At Golden Grove, the earlier steam engine was replaced by a gas engine in 1905. The complete coal-gas installation including the retort, gas holder, purifier, gas engine, a new dynamo and batteries, along with some additional wiring, cost £638.00, the equivalent of about £70,000 today (Cawdor Archives Box 2/234 1905; Box 2/180 Golden

Grove Inventory, May 1908, Carmarthenshire Archives Service).

When the upgraded installation had been completed, Golden Grove had 189 electric lights and a small number of power points (Cawdor Archives, Box 2/234, Carmarthenshire Archives Service). The inclusion of power points may not necessarily be an indication that electric 'power' was being used at that date, however; they were only present in the study, the North Bedroom and its dressing room, and were more than likely intended for table lamps.

The somewhat later installation at Newton House (installed in the late-1920s) used a gas engine and acetylene gas to drive an AC generator. The Newton House installation actually did include power points, showing that within a relatively short period of time the popularity of electric lighting and electrical appliances had grown significantly. In a letter from Newton House to his daughter Muryell, W. Talbot Rice wrote:

> The House is about perfect now. They have lit it with electricity; beautifully done; all standard lights, none from the ceilings and one has 5 in one's bedroom! (letter dated 9th Aug 1927, Newton House Archives).

The acetylene gas producer, gas engine and alternator were all housed in the inner service courtyard, along with the carbide store.

Apart from Golden Grove, Scolton Manor was one of the few country houses in west Wales that generated electricity using steam power, and though the details of the system are sketchy, a specific coal store to serve the engine room and battery house is clearly marked on a plan of the service range (Scolton Manor plan, Pembrokeshire Archives).

The vast majority of country-house installations in Wales still only provided electric lighting. It was not just seen as clean, bright, convenient and safe, but also as 'modern' and 'progressive' in an age when, even in country houses, modernity was being warmly embraced. Electric bedside lights had the added appeal and convenience of being able to be switched on and off at the flick of a switch.

Although the focus of attention remained firmly on electric lighting, there was also growing interest in electrical appliances in the opening decades of the twentieth century. When, for example, the electricity supply was being considered for Nanteos in 1914, the choice of voltage was determined by whether or not electric motors or heating appliances would also be required.

The company in charge of the installation (Furneaux, Riddall and Co., of Southsea) explained the advantages of a 100-volt supply over a 50-volt supply:

> ...for larger plants, especially where motor appliances and small heating apparatus are contemplated, 100 volts is far more convenient...for 50 volt Instalations [sic] such apparatus and appliances would have to be specially made at higher cost and longer delivery. Whereas with 100 volt one has the advantage of being able to procure immediately practically any Motor or heating apparatus (letter dated 9th November 1914, NLW).

The letter went on to list some of the appliances that were available at the time, including electric kettles, electric irons, toasters and vacuum cleaners. It is not known which, if any, appliances were actually purchased when the installation was completed the following year.

Until the spread of the National Grid after the Second World War, the only way those living in country houses could enjoy electric lighting was if they provided it for themselves. Prior to that, and for those unwilling to invest in the new technology, oil lamps and candles were the only means of providing light during the long winter evenings. And even when electricity was installed, candles were still used on special, festive occasions.

With the spread of the National Grid into rural areas, the occupants of more and more country houses began to enjoy the benefits of electric lighting. The National Grid used alternating current, which, along with its use of step-up and step-down transformers, enabled it to distribute high-voltage electricity over long distances economically and efficiently. Mains electricity had a number of advantages over battery systems – not least the fact that lights didn't dim spookily when the load on the batteries increased. It was also available around the clock, and did away with the need to provide a battery house, dynamo and engine, etc. It was also better able to power the growing number of electrical appliances coming onto the market after the Second World War. In a final, vain attempt at maintaining their accustomed levels of comfort and ease, landowners without an independent supply connected to the grid, and those with such a supply abandoned it in favour of the grid.

SERVANT NUMBERS

Fig 79. Clynfyw Servants in 1906.

A ny discussion of the relationship between servant numbers and technology
must at some point attempt to quantify the number of servants involved.
The argument generally put forward is that as long as there were servants
available to complete all the household tasks and chores involved in running a
country house, there was little incentive to invest in domestic technology.

In the eighteenth and nineteenth centuries, the ample supply of
domestic servants in west Wales was helped by the lack of alternative job
opportunities in mills, factories and shops. Domestic service also had
distinct attractions for the sons and daughters of local farmers and villagers;
it provided board and lodgings, companionship, a degree of job security
and regular, though admittedly low, wages. The training given to female
servants also provided them with vital domestic skills that made them
eminently suitable as marriage partners.

Conversely, when servants became more expensive to employ, and it became more difficult to recruit and retain them, it was increasingly necessary to invest in domestic technology. Such investment made country-house owners less reliant on servants, while at the same time making those servants they wished to employ, somewhat easier to recruit. Domestic servants naturally preferred to work in an environment with at least some labour-saving devices. That was especially the case after the First World War when young, working-class men and women had more job opportunities and were less willing to put up with the petty restrictions, hierarchical subservience and demeaning tasks involved in domestic service.

Referring, admittedly, to a somewhat earlier period, Pamela Sambrook makes the point that:

> Owners seem to have been less concerned about the introduction of equipment whose only advantage was that it could save their servants' time and labour – until, that is, the need arose in the late nineteenth century to make a positive effort to attract and keep good servants (1997, pp.2-3)

In the eighteenth century, and for much of the nineteenth century, it was assumed that gentry households would have sufficient servants to ensure that they ran smoothly and efficiently. Accordingly, houses were designed and built with little thought for labour-saving devices and modern domestic technology. As long as the family could live in comfort and ease, such technology was deemed to be largely unnecessary. To provide for all the needs of the family, most country houses needed, as a bare minimum, an indoor staff of a housekeeper, a cook and several housemaids. The size and make-up of the family, its wealth and status also impacted on the number of servants needed to run the household. If the family had babies or young children, nursery maids, tutors and governesses would be required, and would of course swell the servant numbers, albeit often only temporarily.

Then, depending on the wealth and status of the family, there might be a butler, one or more valets, footmen, lady's maids and coachmen. The 1891 census for Stradey Castle is perhaps typical of servant numbers in a large country house in west Wales at the end of the nineteenth century.

Listed on census night were: a governess, butler, footman, cook, lady's maid, under lady's maid, nurse, nursery maid, three housemaids, a kitchen maid and a scullery maid.

Census records first began to be compiled in 1801, and are probably the most reliable, accessible and widely used source available to assess the number of servants in any given household. Due to the 100-year rule, however, they are only currently available for the period up to 1911. Furthermore, before 1851 only very limited information was collected, and while it is possible to glean a great deal of information from census records, they still provide only a very partial picture, and assessing servant numbers based on census records alone is, to say the very least, a fairly inexact science. Not only were census records only compiled in depth from the mid-nineteenth century, but they were compiled only once every ten years. They therefore can only provide a snapshot of a given household at a single, specific point in time. If members of the family (along with their servants) were elsewhere on census night, the information about servant numbers would be missing, skewed or distorted, and if the house was closed-up and left unoccupied for whatever reason, there would be no record of household size at all. Furthermore, the census only listed living-in, domestic servants. Servants, living in nearby villages, estate cottages or on local farms would not be recorded on the census return. Neither would casual servants employed on a temporary or ad hoc basis. Finally, some servants also had multiple roles; for example, that of cook/housekeeper, or grooms who might be expected to act as footmen on special occasions. All these factors can lead to a possible underestimation and distortion of the servant numbers involved.

The census details for 1921 won't become available until 2021, and it is therefore difficult to chart quantitatively the decline in servant numbers during the First World War and the inter-war period. There is, however, strong anecdotal and literary evidence that there was a rapid decline in servant numbers in Welsh country houses in the decades between 1911 and 1931.

The decline during the war was due to military conscription and war work; and, in the inter-war period, to the well-documented drain on country-house fortunes caused by death duties and taxation. That inevitably led to a general tightening of privileged belts, and a reduction in the lavish entertaining of the Edwardian period. Coupled with those financial and social changes, there was also a growing reluctance on the part of the working class to go into 'service'.

Based on the available evidence, it would appear that a typical country house in west Wales in the eighteenth and nineteenth centuries operated with an indoor staff of between eight and fifteen. Of course some inevitably exceeded that number, for example, at Golden Grove in 1780 there were almost twenty indoor servants to look after a family, which at the time was childless (Dyfed County Council, 1982, p.8).

While Golden Grove may have been a little exceptional in terms of the scale of its servant population, it was quite common for servant numbers to far exceed the size of the family they served.

[Servants] were the essential infrastructure of country-house life. An unlimited pool of cheap labour coped with large house parties, balls and theatricals, and an endless round of cooking, cleaning and carrying fuel. Large houses like Bronwydd and Ffynone each had at one time, about twelve household staff to cater for very small families of two, respectively. (Baker-Jones, 1999, p.145).

Although country houses couldn't operate efficiently without a bevy of servants, significant costs were incurred in maintaining such a large workforce. In the mid-nineteenth century, the typical annual wage for a lady's maid was in the region of £16, a cook about £14, and a housemaid about £12 (Horn. 1990, p.211), equivalent today to between £1,300 and £1,800. In addition to their wages, there was the cost of bed and board, livery and medical care, as well as the taxes imposed on households employing servants.

Taxes paid on servants were first introduced in 1777, and though the tax on female servants was repealed in 1792, the tax on male servants remained in place until 1889. That was possibly due to male servants being seen as something of a luxury and extravagance. When first introduced, the tax on male servants was greater than that on female servants. In 1789, for example, the half-yearly tax paid on ten male servants at Golden Grove amounted to just over £10, while the tax on nine female servants was just £2.5s (Cawdor Muniments, 27/2409, 6 April 1789, Carmarthenshire

Archives Service). The tax burden may not have been a major disincentive to employing servants, but coupled with the other costs, it would have made some landowners think twice about gratuitously taking on more staff than was absolutely necessary. At the same time, it provided those who did maintain a large domestic staff with even more kudos, though only if the servants concerned were on plain view to visitors and guests.

The tables provided at Appendix B, admittedly based on only a very limited number of country houses in west Wales, show the broad composition and numbers of domestic staff employed in a range of typical country houses. The lack of available information for some of the houses on certain dates is due to a number of possible factors – for example, the house being unoccupied on census night.

In summary, it would appear that, depending on family size and circumstances, there was remarkably little variation in total servant numbers for specific houses before the First World War, though what very slight variation there was tended to be downward. For example, after Captain James Stewart of Alltyrodyn Mansion died in 1908, the butler, footman, groom, cook and coachman were all dismissed. In their stead, the kitchen maid did the cooking, and only the lady's maid and two housemaids were retained (South Wales Evening Post, 6 June 1979, p.43). There are also some anomalies thrown up by the tables, suggesting either that servants occasionally did tasks other than those listed on the census, or that other people were brought in from outlying areas to complete those tasks. For example, at Nanteos, while a laundry and dairy formed part of the service range, there are no laundry or dairymaids listed on any of the censuses. That suggests that, as at Alltyrodyn, non-resident, local women were employed to work in the dairy and laundry. If so, those undertaking the work would not have appeared on the census returns.

THE KITCHEN GARDEN

If the service range was the focal point of technology in a country house, then the kitchen garden had a similar role in terms of gardening activities. And, as with the service range, the kitchen garden was an essential part of the self-sufficiency of the gentry household. While the home farm provided meat, poultry, milk and eggs, etc., and the wider estate ensured an ample supply of rabbits, fish and game, the kitchen garden produced the basic fruit and vegetables needed to feed the family. It also provided flowers for the house and – most importantly – out of season produce, and rare and exotic fruit:

> The average family's winter fare was limited to fruit and vegetables that grew out of doors and kept well. The gardens of what used to be known as 'families of quality' were, however, expected to transcend these limitations (Campbell, 2005, p.149).

Given the ease with which we can now buy a wide variety of fruit, vegetables, herbs and spices from around the world at almost any time of the year, it is easy to forget just how monotonous eating only seasonal produce would have been. Kitchen gardens provided the gentry with a much wider choice of fruit and vegetables, and even allowed luxuries such as peaches, melons, oranges, pineapples and vines to be grown.

All country houses had kitchen gardens of some description or other, the vast majority of which were enclosed behind high walls. Some country houses had more than one, for example, Alltyrodyn, Aberglasney, and Llanerchaeron, while Middleton Hall even boasted a rare, double-walled kitchen garden. It was a design that not only reduced still further the risk of cold winds entering the inner garden, but also provided a valuable outer ring for sheltered cultivation. Having more than one walled garden encouraged some specialisation to take place – as at Alltyrodyn, where one

111

garden was used primarily for growing cut-flowers for the house, while the other grew fruit and vegetables.

A walled kitchen garden created a micro-climate, ideal for extending the growing season and for protecting rare and delicate plants. It also helped stop pilfering – the gates leading into them were generally locked at night. The walls provided shelter from the wind and, because it was normal practice to line at least the inner wall with brick, they retained the sun's heat much better than stone. Brick walls acted as huge storage heaters, absorbing the heat from the sun during the day and releasing it in the evening as the temperature dropped. The standard height of kitchen-garden walls was about 12 feet high, partly to allow fruit trees to be trained against them and partly to ensure the produce was fully shielded from the wind. Although they often had more than one entrance, these tended to be small, with solid doors to prevent the wind blowing through them.

Walled kitchen gardens were intended to be viewed by the gentry and their visitors. The layout was carefully designed so that on entering or perambulating around them, there were always attractive views to be seen. Pathways criss-crossed the garden and seats were provided for quiet contemplation in its warm, fragrant atmosphere. Walled gardens were also seen as ideal venues for romance and assignations, and were therefore very popular with younger guests visiting country houses. In the walled garden at Nanteos there was even a statue of Cupid (Joel, 2014, p.55). To ensure the gentry's privacy and seclusion when in the garden, the gardeners would leave when members of the family entered or would retire discretely to areas where they would not be seen – and, more importantly, where they would not be able to overhear private conversations.

In an effort to extend the growing season and to raise ever more exotic crops, not only was extensive expertise and knowledge demanded of the head gardener, but greater use of technology was often adopted in the kitchen garden than in the house it served. Such investment was deemed justifiable, even essential, not only to provide the day-to-day fruit and vegetables needed by the household, but also to provide exotic fruit and out-of-season vegetables for the family and their guests. A well-managed kitchen garden therefore met all the gentry's key demands; it provided pleasure, prestige and recreation.

As a general rule, kitchen gardens were built as close to the service range as possible, so that fruit, vegetables and flowers could be delivered there quickly and in a fresh, undamaged state. Close proximity to the house also meant that members of the family had only a short distance to walk in order to enjoy the kitchen garden's varied pleasures and attractions. However, kitchen gardens were seldom placed where they could be seen from the main house. The gentry may have enjoyed all the benefits of a kitchen garden, but they would not have wanted to see their workers toiling in them, nor did they find vast expanses of bare brick aesthetically pleasing. To gain the maximum benefits from a walled garden, the layout, size and orientation were vitally important considerations in the planning process. South-facing walls, for example, provided the best location for wall-trained fruit trees. The overall size of the garden was determined by the owner (with advice from his head gardener), but the optimum size was generally between 1.5 and 5 acres (Campbell, 2005, p.30). They were almost invariably rectangular in shape, with the longer walls being on an east-west axis so as to gain the most heat and light from the sun.

Fig 80. One of the dipping ponds at Llanerchaeron.

After due consideration had been given to the construction and orientation of the kitchen garden, the next key requirement was a plentiful supply of water for irrigation. Large quantities of water were needed during the growing season, and shallow wells, rainwater butts, and dipping ponds were all used to ensure a reliable and adequate supply.

Fig 81. A second dipping pond at Llanerchaeron.

Dipping ponds retained water channelled into them from nearby springs and streams, and their practical purpose was to enable gardeners to fill watering cans as quickly and easily as possible, but dipping ponds were also designed as much for their aesthetic appeal as for their practical use.

GLASSHOUSES

Because of their ability to provide shelter from cold winds and to act as sun traps, walled kitchen gardens enabled far more delicate plants to be grown than would otherwise have been possible. They also helped to extend the growing season. Another way of extending the season and the range of crops cultivated was to grow them behind glass. Basically, that simply involved building a glass lean-to against one of the inner walls, thereby increasing the level of solar gain and the heat within them. A less common way of protecting plants and promoting their growth was to use hot walls. Hot walls were constructed by building a network of flues within the fabric of the wall. The flues were heated by fire grates at the base of the wall, with the heat from the flues permeating the walls around them. Hot walls were not used extensively in west Wales, but there is visible evidence of them still in a few kitchen gardens today – for example, at Llanerchaeron. Hot walls were used primarily to protect plants from frost damage. They were not really intended for round-the-year use, though trees grown against them benefited from the heat released and produced fruit much earlier in the season. Because managing and controlling the hot-air flues was difficult, time-consuming and not particularly efficient, hot walls ultimately went out of fashion, with their usage really only extending between the 1780s and 1880s (Campbell, 2005, p.60).

Combining the benefits of a glass lean-to and artificial heating into a single structure, a heated glasshouse (or stove house as they were often called) was the next logical step. The heat was provided by large-bore water pipes circulating within the glasshouse. The water in the pipes was heated by a coal-fired boiler,

Fig 82. Heating pipes in a glasshouse at Llanerchaeron.

114

placed outside the glasshouse to reduce the risk of plants being damaged by coal fumes.

Heated glasshouses were at first used to boost the growth of fairly mundane plants, but they were soon being used to cultivate more unusual produce, such as oranges, orchids and vines – the sort of plants that the Welsh climate would otherwise have made almost impossible to grow.

The gentry's desire to grow exotic fruit and flowers may initially have been prompted by the 'grand tour' of Mediterranean Europe that was completed by many members of the wealthy gentry in the eighteenth and nineteenth centuries. The grand tour not only encouraged the gentry to bring back paintings and statues to adorn their country houses, but it also gave them a taste for Mediterranean fruit and flowers. In time, that led them to cultivate such plants on their own estates, and the ability to do so came to be seen as an important feature of country-house living. It even led, occasionally, to intense, horticultural rivalry between families. Growing rare and exotic plants in the cool, wet climate of Wales was exceptionally challenging, and inevitably led to the use of specially designed heated structures. Those evolved during the eighteenth and nineteenth centuries into the orangeries, vineries and pineries that are now frequently found decaying in country-house kitchen gardens across west Wales.

ORANGERIES

Specialisation strongly influenced the overall size and design of such buildings. That is particularly the case with the orangery at Margam, where the emphasis on growing orange trees determined the size of the building, its layout and even the size of its doors.

The Margam orangery was built in the late-eighteenth century by Thomas Mansel Talbot to rehouse an existing collection of orange trees. At the time, it was unrivalled in terms of its size, grandeur and the facilities it offered. It measured some 327 feet in length and was heated by underfloor ducting, with flues in the rear wall. Its large doorways at the rear of the building were tall enough to allow the orange trees (some over 20 feet high and 18 feet wide) to be wheeled outside in the summer. Ultimately, more than a hundred trees were housed in the orangery, all planted in portable boxes for ease of movement.

The added bonus of the Margam orangery was that once the orange trees had been taken outdoors, it could be used as a spacious, indoor facility for summer balls and general entertaining. Even in the winter months, when the orange trees had been returned, the pavilions at either end of the orangery could be used for recreation. The east pavilion contained statues brought back by Thomas Talbot from the grand tour, and the west pavilion had a library, marble fireplace, alabaster vases and models of Roman buildings (Woods and Warren, 1990, p.81). The pavilions provided elegant and sophisticated settings in which to take tea, read or simply enjoy polite conversation. Even in the depths of winter, the heated central orangery provided a pleasant environment for an afternoon stroll.

Fig 83. The orangery at Margam Park.

The ability to serve home grown oranges to one's guests was clearly a way of demonstrating wealth, status and hospitality. Oranges were not the only fruit, however, and while Margam was exceptional in the scale of its orangery, it was not alone within the region in nurturing citrus fruit. Tangerines, for example, were grown at Alltyrodyn Mansion in the 1830s, and many other country houses in Wales grew grapes, peaches and pineapples. There was, for example, a peach house at Stradey Castle, a melon house and vinery at Nanteos, while Middleton Hall had both a peach house and a pinery.

Pineapples were particularly prized because of their flavour and spectacular appearance. Middleton Hall pineapples, for example, were so highly valued that they were loaned out to other gentry families for display purposes when entertaining.

Mrs John Farrar (1791–1870), describing her childhood in Castle Hall, Pembrokeshire, and her father's enthusiasm for growing rare and exotic plants, wrote:

Seven acres of ornamental grounds and gardens gave my father ample scope for his love of improving and embellishing the place; he made ugly slopes into pretty terraces, formed new land in front

116

of the house, built an orangery eighty feet long and twenty feet high, entirely of iron and glass, and filled it with the finest orange, lemon, and citron-trees…He made pineries too, – three houses, hot, hotter, and hottest, – in which three hundred fine, large pine-apples were produced in one year…All these improvements, with the high cultivation of English gardening, not usually practised in Wales, made Castle Hall a show-place. The orangery and the pinery were a great novelty in Pembrokeshire, and I remember being very tired of showing them to our visitors (Farrar, 1865, p.53).

With the possible exception of the Margam orangery, most orangeries, pineries and vineries were working buildings, specifically designed and run to preserve and pamper fragile plants that needed over-wintering. Sophisticated heating, ventilating and irrigating systems were needed to support them, as well as some means of controlling and adjusting humidity levels. Although the head gardener would normally determine the size, shape and orientation of such buildings, the heating and ventilating systems would usually be provided and installed by specialist manufacturers. In the late nineteenth century, Messenger & Co., of Loughborough was one of the leading manufacturers of heating and ventilation systems for vineries and orangeries, and provided equipment for many country houses in Wales, including Hafod and Margam.

The correct level of ventilation to suit specific plants and weather conditions was essential for successful cultivation. Rooftop ventilation was particularly important because it didn't create a draught, and helped prevent the build-up of humidity and moisture that could damage plants preferring dry heat. In horticultural circles, it was widely accepted that ventilation should extend continuously along the entire length of the apex. In large glasshouses, mechanical winding mechanisms were provided, operated by cranking handles attached to levers that opened and closed the roof-level windows. Considering the size and height of many glasshouse ranges, it was an invaluable piece of technology. Without it, each rooftop window would have had to be opened individually – a lengthy and tedious process. It would also have involved manipulating large step ladders in very enclosed spaces, which could easily have resulted in broken panes of glass and damaged plants.

The total cost of a typical glasshouse rose dramatically when including the cost of heating and ventilation systems. The peach house at Stradey

Castle, built in 1874 by John Weeks & Co of London, cost £732, equivalent to about £72,000 today. It included:

Wood, Glass framing, glazing, painting, and seventeen ventilators, along with machinery to open and close all the windows and shutters:	452.0.0
Peach Stages throughout and wiring to back wall:	78.0.0
Hot-water apparatus:	96.0.0
Tanks and Connections:	30.0.0
Iron Trellis Paths:	76.0.0

The Stradey Castle peach house was a very sophisticated structure. It was compartmentalised and enabled the hot-water heating system to heat all, or just one compartment, at any one time. Rainwater was collected from the roof via gutters and stored in tanks that were all connected together (Stradey Castle archives, letter from the head gardener Mr. R. Robertson, dated 13 November 1874, Carmarthenshire Archives Service).

PINERIES

Pineapples are indigenous to South America, and were such a novelty in Europe in the seventeenth and eighteenth centuries that they were given as high-status gifts to royalty and senior statesmen. Paintings were made of these presentations, and when the fruits were first successfully grown on an estate in Britain, there were celebrations that almost befit the birth of the first male heir (Campbell, 2005, pp.160-2). Pineapples were the pinnacle of exotic fruit grown in Wales. Not only were they delicious, but the challenges they presented in terms of cultivation ensured their rarity and made them a potent symbol of an estate's horticultural ability to grow them successfully. They also provided a decorative centrepiece at country-house dinners throughout the eighteenth and nineteenth centuries.

Pineapples can be grown from seed, rooted suckers or from the crown of a mature pineapple. They need heat and moisture to thrive, and pineries had to maintain a year-round minimum, ambient temperature – indeed, even the soil in which they grew had to be kept warm. In the early-eighteenth century, the method most widely adopted was to grow the pineapples in pots in pine-pits during the summer and transfer them to heated pineries in the winter. The pine pits were filled with tanners' bark (crushed oak bark soaked in water) or horse dung, both of which released heat during fermentation. That was the system adopted at Middleton Hall, though a slightly more sophisticated system was adopted at Stackpole Court, where, the pine pits were heated by a subterranean boiler house. Pineapples take about eighteen months to grow, so they had to be transferred back and forth between the pine pits and pinery during the growing cycle. Ultimately, the pine pits and pineries were combined into a single, long, low, heated building. The whole process of regulating the heat and humidity required great skill, judgement and expertise on the part of the head gardener.

Fig 84. The restored pineapple house at Scolton Manor.

Middleton Hall and Stackpole Court were not, however, the only country houses in the region to grow pineapples; they were also grown at Scolton Manor, Cyfarthfa Castle in Mid-Glamorgan and at Penpont in Powys.

VINERIES

Grapes were easier to grow than pineapples, but they were still a challenge to cultivate successfully and had to be grown behind glass in heated vineries. Only the sweet varieties of vines were grown – those suitable for eating and as table decorations, rather than vines intended for winemaking. As with other such status symbols, country-house owners took great pleasure in showing off their vineries to their visitors and guests. The pleasure was probably mutual; on a visit to Cresselly in 1840, Joseph Romilly noted in his diary his delight at visiting the vinery to eat grapes (Morris, 1998, p.89).

Vineries, as with other specialist garden structures, were carefully designed to meet the requirements of the particular plants being grown. They had sloping glass walls to gain the maximum amount of heat from the sun – even late in the year when it was low in the sky. The temperature inside was slowly increased during the growing season from about 10 degrees centigrade (50F) to 27 degrees centigrade (80F), and evaporating pans were used to create just the right humidity. It was anticipated that such an investment in facilities and nurture would be rewarded, and Victorian and Edwardian gardeners were expected to supply their employers with hothouse grapes throughout the year (Campbell, 2005, p.179).

Janet Joel describes the Nanteos vinery as:

…the largest structure in the [kitchen] garden, the stone wall measuring 18.9 metres in length, and the frame measuring 13.43 metres in length. It has seven steps leading up to the vinery door. Within the vinery there are 12 weights enclosed into wooden slots for opening and closing the glazed frames. A flue for the boiler is also located on the wall. A well is located in the centre of the floor which measures 0.85 metres x 1.20 metres with a terracotta pipe overflow. On the south exterior of the vinery, on the brick base there are 11 rooting arches, each measuring 0.80 meters. The rooting system of the vines would have been planted outside and the foliage would have been trained through the arches into the vinery (Joel, 2014, p.31).

This method of planting the roots of the vines outside the heated vinery was quite common in the nineteenth century, but it was later found that they could grow just as successfully if planted within the vinery.

CONSERVATORIES

It was an obvious and logical step to move from growing exotic fruit and plants in a heated orangery or vinery some distance from the house, to creating a 'conservatory' accessed directly from it, thereby avoiding the need even to step outdoors to enjoy its varied pleasures. The term conservatory was first coined by John Evelyn in the seventeenth century, as a means of 'conserving' rare and delicate botanical specimens, but by the eighteenth century they were seen as warm, dry living spaces, with the added appeal of containing fragrant and attractive plants. The emphasis had changed from nurture to recreation. It is easy to see the appeal of a conservatory in west Wales, an area renowned for its rain and drizzle. A conservatory promoted a feeling of being outdoors, without the risk of actually getting wet. Although by no means did all country houses in Wales have conservatories, they were undoubtedly a popular feature of many. Middleton Hall had a conservatory that was over 30 feet long; Alltyferin had one; and a small one was even created on the upper floor of Newton House, from where it overlooked the formal gardens; and Cilwendeg had two (one attached to each wing of the house). The Cilwendeg conservatories (still in existence) are impressive Victorian structures, which replaced earlier Georgian ones.

Conservatories provided yet another opportunity for displaying a family's wealth and style, and by the Victorian period they were definitely a platform to show off one's horticultural skills, as well as one's flair for decoration and interior design:

> The Victorian conservatory…was part of the house; it was crammed with plants, just as the drawing room was crammed with furniture…It was a jewel casket of brilliant hues, where biggest or rarest was thought to be best…To this vibrant array of foliage and flowers, the Victorians added further decoration. Pots for flowers were carved or glazed…Flagstones, as used in greenhouses for two

hundred years, were overlaid with tiles…often in elaborate Italian or Moorish patterns. Cast-iron grilles covering hot-water pipes were stamped with swirls and squares; cast-iron columns were twisted, grooved, garlanded or made classical with capitals; flowery baskets hung from curling brackets; fountains and statues completed the decoration (Woods and Warren, 1990, p.164).

Victorian conservatories were multi-functional. They were seen not just as a way of building up collections of rare and exotic plants, but also as an important recreational space where tea could be taken and quiet contemplation could be enjoyed. Like kitchen gardens, they were also a place where romance could be fostered away from prying eyes. May Woods describes that specific aspect of a conservatory's role particularly eloquently:

Fig 85. Part of the tiled floor and grille in one of the conservatories at Cilwendeg.

It is one of the paradoxes of many a Victorian conservatory that a building designed to catch the sun was turned into a gloomy place by dense planting. A thick canopy of overhead foliage certainly helped to give both shade and the jungle atmosphere, but denied the attraction of sunlight. The darkness, however, brought its own excitement. The very lushness of the vegetation, the dimness of the shadows, the warm heavy-scented air, and the twisting, turning paths were ideal for romance. Proposals of marriage – and perhaps others too – were thought appropriately made in the conservatory, a sensuous haven in the strict Victorian Household. How propitious the big conservatories must have been for amorous young men; and how understandable that young ladies should discover a sudden, overpowering interest in botany (Woods and Warren, 1990, p.165).

ICEHOUSES

Romance and recreation apart, the primary aim of the conservatory, the kitchen garden and the heated glasshouse was to cultivate rare and delicate plants, and to extend the growing season. Another way of providing out-of-season treats was by salting or smoking meat, or by using ice to preserve fish, game and vegetables. Ice could also of course be used to chill drinks in summer, and make ice cream. In the eighteenth and nineteenth centuries, before ice could be imported from colder climes or manufactured commercially, one way of providing ice in the summer was to collect it in the winter and store it in specially built icehouses. Icehouses have been included in this discussion of kitchen gardens because it was the head gardener who was normally responsible for the success or failure

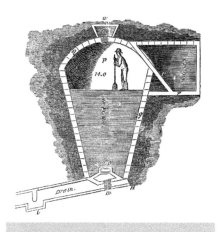

Fig 86. A schematic illustration of an icehouse, showing the basic construction, the meltwater drain and the method of tamping down the ice.

of the icehouse, and because icehouses had an important place in feeding and entertaining the gentry.

Fig 87. The entrance passage in the ice house at Middleton Hall.

Insulation was an essential feature of successful icehouse construction. Icehouses were usually built more or less underground on north-facing hillsides. They were egg-shaped, with brick-lined cavity walls and an entrance passage with one or more, thick, tightly fitting doors to form a sort of airlock; all features deliberately intended to maximise the insulation of the icehouse. A drainage channel at the base took away any melt water, which if not removed would have speeded up the thawing process. An icehouse would cost between about £200 and £300 to build, the equivalent of about £25,000 today, so its construction was not undertaken lightly and it was clearly expected to provide some significant benefits to those investing in it. The ice from icehouses was used, in conjunction with zinc-lined ice-cabinets in kitchens, to help preserve fresh fruit, fish, poultry and vegetables (Campbell, 2005, pp.260-61). It was also used to cool drinks in summer, provide desserts and ice sculptures at balls and banquets, and even, in extremis, to treat fevers.

Fig 88. A photograph showing the rebate where the inner door fitted in the entrance passage of the Middleton Hall icehouse.

The ice was collected from frozen ponds and lakes in winter, and taken to the icehouse by horse and cart. Once there, it was rammed into the ice chamber to remove any air pockets. Additional insulation in the icehouse was provided by straw, either to separate layers of ice, or as a top covering. Icehouses had to be as dry as possible before fresh

Fig 89. The entrance passage to the Newton House icehouse.

ice was loaded into them, so the doors were left open to help dry them out and ventilate them. Fires and quicklime were sometimes also used to drive out any residual moisture in the chamber. Most icehouses were able to store between 20 and 30 tons of ice.

The ability to provide chilled drinks and luxury foods out of season was a way of enjoying life to the full and of demonstrating a family's wealth and sophistication. Ice from the icehouse did not, however, come into direct contact with the food and drink being served. It was far too contaminated with grass, mud, or possibly even animal droppings to be used in that way. Instead, fish, meat and game were preserved by being placed in containers packed around with ice. Similarly, ice from the icehouse was used only to aid the chilling process in the production of ice cream – it was never actually added directly to the mix. In the same way, ice from the icehouse was not actually dropped into drinks to chill them, but was packed around bottles in wine chillers and ice buckets.

Icehouses were surprisingly common on country estates in west Wales, with surviving examples at Newton House, Nanteos, Middleton Hall, Picton Castle and Hafod.

Fig 90. The icehouse at Newton House.

As with other commercially produced items such as bread and beer, which ultimately led to the abandonment of estate bakeries and brew houses, ice 'manufactured' in Britain or imported from America or Scandinavia signalled the death knell of the estate icehouse. Transporting large quantities of ice cheaply and easily was made possible by steam ships, the spreading railway network, better roads and the use of motor vehicles. Collecting ice from ponds and lakes, and filling icehouses was unpleasant, labour-intensive work, and the unreliable weather meant that it could never be guaranteed that lakes and ponds would freeze over as and when required.

Kitchen-garden technology, in all its various guises, added significantly to the pleasures and recreational opportunities enjoyed by the Welsh gentry. It helped provide variety to tempt tired and jaded palates during the long winter months, a visual display in the summer and treats throughout the year.

CONCLUSION

In essence, the long-lasting appeal of 'traditional' country-house technology was its reliability and simplicity. Chamber pots for sanitation, logs for heat, candles for light, and washbowls and hip baths for washing and bathing were incapable of malfunctioning. Provided there were ample servants to undertake the chores associated with them, comfort and convenience were assured. For much of the period 1750–1930, the gentry's pursuit of pleasure, comfort and prestige remained undimmed, and the country house was a key element in achieving those aims. As the pretensions of individual families grew, so did the size of their country houses. The desire to outshine their neighbours – in terms of elegant surroundings, comfort, splendour and hospitality – led to the large-scale rebuilding or relocating of manor houses. It also often led to previously modest, Georgian houses being enlarged by the addition of new wings, frontages, entrance lobbies, billiard rooms and conservatories.

Domestic technology, though often hidden from view, also figured prominently in the process of gaining the most comfort, pleasure and prestige. The social elite within the region were intimately aware of each other's lifestyles, wealth and possessions. They wined and dined each other regularly, attended balls and parties in each other's homes, and frequently stayed overnight. They were certainly aware of any technical improvements and innovations introduced in a neighbour's house, even if the neighbour in question didn't show them off or boast about them. If one gentry family introduced some new form of technology, for example, electric lighting, it would soon encourage other landowners in the area to emulate them.

Such large-scale investment, in addition to the lavish entertaining deemed necessary for leading figures in society, was just about sustainable when there was a steady income from the estate to meet such costs. In the early decades of the twentieth century, however, when the balance between income and expenditure began to tip in the wrong direction, excessively

126

large, sprawling country houses became problematic in terms of upkeep, or even basic maintenance. Pleasure and prestige may still have been important to the Welsh gentry in the Edwardian and inter-war periods, but the pursuit of a hedonistic lifestyle was often achieved only by neglecting the care and repair of the basic structure and fabric of the family home.

In the inter-war period especially, declining estate incomes and greater difficulty in recruiting and retaining domestic staff had a noticeable and adverse impact on the country-house lifestyle. Living comfortably in houses designed to be run by a small army of servants was only possible with greater reliance on modern domestic technology. Similarly, changing social perceptions and the growing use of private motorcars gave members of the family more freedom and greater independence, and made keeping coachmen, grooms and chauffeurs largely unnecessary. Commercial dairies, laundries and breweries made service ranges largely redundant, while imported fruit such as oranges, peaches and pineapples meant that heated greenhouses became almost obsolete, and greengrocers willing to deliver to outlying areas meant that kitchen gardens became less important in fulfilling the household's day-to-day requirements. In addition, the introduction of even a very rudimentary telephone network, meant that country landowners were able to contact suppliers quickly and effortlessly to arrange deliveries. These changes meant that it was no longer necessary to employ large numbers of domestic servants. Service ranges were abandoned, greenhouses fell into disrepair and kitchen gardens became overgrown. Woodland walks, pleasure gardens, boating lakes and water features received less attention and gradually declined into disuse.

The other significant change that impacted on the country-house lifestyle in the inter-war period was the decline of lives devoted almost entirely to pleasure. The sons and daughters of the gentry were better educated and more qualified than ever before, and sought careers and greater personal independence. They were no longer expected to while their time away in idleness; social and financial pressures encouraged them to take up full-time, professional occupations. That in turn, often meant that because younger members of the local elite left home to take up careers in towns and cities, those actually resident in country houses dwindled in number. Furthermore, as more and more romantic relationships were formed away from the local area, the opportunities for courtship – previously such a feature of country house entertaining – declined in importance. The social round of visits, balls, house parties, hunting, croquet and tennis simply faded away.

In the inter-war period, and more especially after the Second World War, the upkeep of a large country house became increasingly costly. Heating, lighting, decorating, repairing and maintaining a large country house demanded an equally large income, and the twentieth century saw income from land in serious decline. Coupled with death duties and increased taxation, that inevitably led country landowners to begin the slow, painful process of retrenchment, during which, in order to retain some sort of presence in their ancestral homes, country-house owners often moved into just a suite of rooms in the former, sprawling manor house. Others decamped entirely, selling off their estates, or leaving them to crumble away until they were uninhabitable. That led ultimately to many such houses becoming romantic ruins, overgrown by trees and vegetation, sinking slowly back into the landscape. Others were saved by being opened to the public, taken over by the National Trust, or turned into boarding schools, museums, hotels and nursing homes. Compared to the extraordinarily large number of country houses in west Wales in the eighteenth and nineteenth centuries, only a few of the relatively smaller ones are still in private ownership today, thanks largely to the dedication and sacrifices of the present owners.

For the gentry at least, those halcyon days of pleasure, comfort and prestige made possible by a bevy of servants supported by slowly evolving technology, are now largely just a fond memory, viewed through faded photographs, dusty archives, and the rare journal or diary.

Appendix A

Houses discussed in the text

The information presented below, relating to individual families and houses, is – to a large extent – based on the three seminal works by Francis Jones: *Historic Cardiganshire Homes and Their Families; Historic Carmarthenshire Homes and Their Families;* and *Historic Pembrokeshire Homes and Their Families*. Other sources consulted in compiling this gazetteer of country houses in west Wales include the *Buildings of Wales* series of books, especially those devoted to Carmarthenshire, Ceredigion and Pembrokeshire. The material relating to technology is covered in more detail and more extensively in the body of the text than here, but some of it is repeated here in abbreviated form to provide a more rounded, contextual description, linked to specific country houses.

ABERGLASNEY, CARMARTHENSHIRE

(The Aberglasney gardens are open to the public.)

Fig. 92. Aberglasney.

BACKGROUND HISTORY

The Aberglasney estate and house was bought by Bishop Rudd (Bishop of St. Davids) in the early-seventeenth century. The estate itself was quite modest in size and, as was often the case with country estates in west Wales, the limited income from such a small estate was a perennial problem for subsequent owners. Fortunately for the Bishop he didn't rely on farm rentals to finance his building work; instead he drew on his income from the Church to fund day-to-day running costs and pay for the rebuilding of the original house.

As well as rebuilding the house, Bishop Rudd began laying out the grounds, including the cloister garden, which at that time would have been used for growing medicinal herbs and plants. The next significant building phase was in 1710, when Robert Dyer, a Carmarthen lawyer, bought the house and gave it a more up-to-date appearance in the Queen Anne style.

Like Bishop Rudd, Dyer was able to fund his country-house lifestyle from external sources. When his son, also called Robert, inherited the estate in 1752, he made further changes to the house, including raising the height of the main hall (by removing some of the first-floor bedrooms). However, in 1798, with debts mounting, the house was put up for sale and was ultimately bought in 1803 by Thomas Philips. Philips had made his fortune with the East India Company so was also not reliant on the estate for his income. He spent lavishly on extensive redecoration and an impressive Portico to the main entrance. On his death in 1824, the house was inherited by his nephew, John Walters, and subsequently John's daughter, Marianne. On her marriage in 1872, she moved to Derbyshire with her husband and the house was let out to tenants until they returned in 1902. Within five years of their return her husband had died, and she left Aberglasney unoccupied to spend the rest of her life in London, where she died in 1939.

TECHNOLOGY

Aberglasney mansion is a prime example of a country house where the owners' lengthy absences, especially during a period when new technology was being widely introduced into country houses, led to significant underinvestment. It is difficult now to assess with confidence what forms of technology were introduced into the house, or when they were introduced. There is virtually no surviving physical evidence of domestic technology, and little in the way of supporting documentary material. However, there was an abundant (possibly, too abundant) supply of water to the house and gardens. Leats and drains were used to provide an ample supply for the house, irrigation for the kitchen garden and water for the fishpond.

An interesting and unusual feature of Aberglasney Mansion is the culverted drainage system running beneath the house. Water from high ground behind the house was channelled into a sump, and then under the house into a large fish pond. The sump was intended to stop the house from being inundated by water during periods of heavy rainfall, possibly because the drain under the house was unable to carry storm water off adequately.

Water for the service range was originally obtained from a well (still in existence) in the kitchen, and the indoor plumbing was almost entirely confined to the service range. Although it is possible that some water closets were installed in the main house, there is no evidence of there being any bathrooms before the Second World War. It was only after 1945 that electricity was installed. It was a direct current system with a belt-driven dynamo and a single-cylinder diesel engine. The diesel engine, generator and batteries were all housed in a purpose-built building to the rear of the house, near the service range. Central heating was never installed at Aberglasney and the house was heated solely by open fires. A privy leat for servants was built near the service range, with the privy waste away being discharged into a nearby water course.

In the garden, a large vinery (20 feet by 40 feet) was built in the nineteenth century, which was kept at the correct temperature by a sophisticated ventilation system and cast-iron water pipes heated from a nearby stove. To help drain the pleasure gardens, rills channelled water into the fish pond, the walled gardens and the dipping pond.

ALLTYRODYN MANSION, CEREDIGION

(Alltyrodyn Mansion is in private ownership.)

Fig 93. Alltyrodyn Mansion.

BACKGROUND HISTORY

David Lloyd (1748 – 1822) inherited the original house and estate of Alltyrodyn from his father, and during his lifetime built up an extensive library, largely devoted to genealogy. He and his wife Elizabeth (d. 1805) had two sons (David and John) and three daughters (Ann, Justinia and Elizabeth). When David (the eldest son) died, his younger brother, John, inherited the estate, and the house was remodelled for him in the late-1820s. He died, unmarried, in 1841 and the estate passed to his cousin Anne, who had previously married John Lloyd-Davies (1801-60), an Aberystwyth solicitor. Anne died soon after the marriage and her widower remarried a wealthy Englishwoman, Elizabeth Hardwick. They had a son, Arthur (1827-1852), who was killed in a riding accident, and it was Arthur's son, John Lloyd Davies (1850-1878, who ultimately inherited the estate in 1860 (on the death of his grandfather). John squandered much of the estate on drink, eventually transferring the estate to James Allen, a London solicitor's clerk. John Lloyd Davies' sister subsequently went through Chancery to regain the estate, but by then the estate's debts meant that she had to sell it in 1881. It was bought by Captain James Stewart JP and his wife, Eveline. James Stewart was High Sheriff in 1896 and died in 1908. His eldest son, Lieutenant James Alexander Logan Stewart, (1883-1915) was killed at Ypres during the First World War (Jones, 2004, pp.19-21). The Stewart family sold the house and estate in 1947.

TECHNOLOGY

There was an extensive service range at Alltyrodyn Mansion, similar in design and scale to that at Llanerchaeron. It included wet and dry laundries, a bake house, dairy, brushing room, coal store, kitchen and scullery. And before the mansion was connected to the National Grid in 1955, the service range also housed the diesel engine, generator and batteries. Just outside the service range was a bell tower used to call the gardener's boy to take the cook's orders for the day's fruit and vegetables.

The water supply for the house was from a spring impounded by a weir on high ground above the house. The water was carried from the weir to a holding tank, from where it was fed by gravity to cisterns in the roof of the house and to the service range. When the house was sold in 1929, there were two bathrooms and a single WC serving three double bedrooms with dressing rooms and four single bedrooms. It must be presumed that, even by that date, there was still great reliance placed on the traditional forms of technology with regard to sanitation, washing and bathing. The drains from the house were fed into a ha-ha in front of the house, which discharged into the Afon Clettwr.

In the grounds of the house was a plunge bath fed by spring water, two walled gardens, a small orangery and a glasshouse heated by an external boiler.

There were two privy leats in the grounds, at some distance from each other. One was for the gardeners and one was for the indoor servants. The indoor servants' privy had separate cubicles for male and female members of staff, and for the sake of even greater decorum there was a wall separating the entrances to the two. In the twentieth century, a water closet was installed in at least one of the two cubicles.

In its heyday in the mid-nineteenth century, Alltyrodyn was the largest estate in South Cardiganshire (Lloyd, et al, 2006, p.569).

Bronwydd, Ceredigion

(Bronwydd is now in ruins.)

Fig 94. Bronwydd.

Background history

The mansion of Bronwydd was built between 1850 and 1853 in the gothic style, on the site of an earlier, sixteenth-century manor house. It was built by Thomas Lloyd, who inherited the estate from his father in 1845. At various times, Thomas Lloyd served as a Justice of the Peace, High Sheriff of Cardiganshire and a Member of Parliament. He spent lavishly on the creation of a baronial mansion, and sought to adopt the lifestyle and trappings he felt befitted his high rank and status. He was made a baronet in 1863 and on his death in 1877, he was succeeded by his son, Marteine Owen Mowbray Lloyd. As well as inheriting the house and an estate of 7,946 acres, Marteine inherited huge debts of £94,000 and a taste for lavish living that was well beyond his means. By selling off large parts of the estate, he attempted to reduce the debt burden while still living in quite a grand manner. Sir Marteine's only son, Martin, was killed in the First World War; and because the government deemed that

Martin had already succeeded to the property by the time of his death, Sir Marteine not only had to pay death duties on the property but also the succession duty. Sir Marteine and his wife died in 1933 and 1937, respectively, and the house was sold.

TECHNOLOGY

Given the desire to create and retain a medieval ambience, it is not surprising that Bronwydd relied heavily on traditional forms of technology in terms of heating, lighting and sanitation. However, a piped hot and cold water supply (along with two bathrooms and, possibly, two water closets) was installed in 1894, and electric lighting in 1925. It used a petrol engine to drive a DC dynamo, with the electricity generated being stored in a nearby battery house. The service range included a kitchen, scullery, dairy, laundry and servants' hall.

CILWENDEG, PEMBROKESHIRE

(Cilwendeg is in private ownership.)

Fig 95. Cilwendeg.

BACKGROUND HISTORY

The present house is a rebuilding of a previous smaller house on the same site. The bulk of the rebuilding work took place in the 1780s for Morgan Jones, whose wealth came from fees charged by the Skerry lighthouse. After Morgan Jones's death in 1826, the house passed to his nephew – also called Morgan Jones – who spent lavishly on enlarging the house, and adding the two conservatories at either end of the building. He died in 1840 aged 55 and the house passed to his sister, Jane Martha Jones. She continued to live in the house until her death in 1864, when the house passed to her niece, Margaretta Sutton Jones. She chose not to live there, but instead employed a bailiff to manage the estate for her. Margaretta died in 1870 and, in 1884, her husband sold the estate to the Saunders-Davies family of Pentre. Fanny Saunders-Davies spent a considerable amount of money renovating the house, replacing the earlier conservatories, adding a billiard room and porte-cochere. The house was leased out until 1898, when Arthur Saunders-Davies (Fanny's son) married and moved from Pentre to Cilwendeg. On his death in 1902, his wife and family moved back to Pentre, and the house was again leased out – at one time to the Colby's of Ffynone while their house was being renovated. The house was sold in 1936 for £1,500 to Daniel Daniel J.P., a coal owner from Neath.

TECHNOLOGY

During the entire period 1780–1930, the house was heated solely by coal and log fires, and for most of that time it was lit by candles and oil lamps. Gas lighting was introduced into the house in about 1920, using an acetylene gas producer installed in what had previously been the service-range laundry and dairy.

The water supply to the servicer range was initially piped from springs above the house to a ground-floor storage cistern close to the scullery and kitchen. Drinking water, however, was carried by hand from a spring below the house. There is also some evidence that the water supply may at some time have been supplemented by rainwater storage cisterns in the loft. By 1906, two bathrooms had been installed, with the hot-water supply provided by an independent boiler (separate from the late-nineteenth century kitchen range). Hot and cold running water was also supplied to the kitchen, butler's pantry and maids' closet. A water closet was installed to serve the bedrooms, and another to serve the smoking room and billiard room. When the bathrooms were installed, a petrol engine was used to pump water to the upper floors of the house. By then, the water was being impounded in a small reservoir/pond close to the home-farm buildings. From the pond, it was filtered, before being pumped to a storage tank in the loft. The petrol engine driving the pump was replaced by an electric motor in the 1940s, when mains electricity reached the house.

A plunge bath has recently been discovered in a room close to the billiard room.

The house-drains originally discharged into a stream close to the main house, but with the introduction of bathrooms and water closets in the early-twentieth century, the foul drainage was channelled into a septic tank. The effluent from the tank then either went into a soakaway or, possibly, a nearby stream.

FFYNONE, PEMBROKESHIRE

(Ffynone is in private ownership.)

Fig 96. Ffynone.

BACKGROUND HISTORY

The Ffynone estate came into the possession of the Colby family in 1752. The original, early-sixteenth century house was replaced by John Colby in the late-eighteenth century by one a few hundred yards away, but with more panoramic views. John Nash was the architect, and the work was completed between 1792 and 1795. While the core of the present house is by Nash, extensive additional work was completed by Inigo Thomas between 1902 and 1907.

When John Vaughan Colby, a direct descendent of the original John Colby, died in 1919, his daughter, Aline Margaret, inherited the house and estate. She married C.J.H. Spence-Jones, who subsequently changed his name to Colby. In 1927, the estate was sold to Daniel Daniel, the High Sheriff of Pembrokeshire, and, in 1988, to Earl Lloyd George, the grandson of David Lloyd George (the Liberal politician).

TECHNOLOGY

The original sixteenth-century house was built over a spring. When the new house was built, it continued to be served by the same spring. Water from the spring was fed into two holding ponds nearby, from where it supplied the house, a fountain and the kitchen garden. It is unclear how water from the spring/ponds was accessed by the service range of the new house, as the holding ponds are at a lower level than the house itself. It is possible that water was simply carried by hand to the service range. Alternatively, rainwater from the roof may have been collected in ground-level storage cisterns, but there is no direct evidence to support that suggestion. The water supply to the house was dramatically improved in the early-twentieth century, however, when a spring, high on a hill on the other side of the valley, was used to supply the house with water. The spring was fed into two underground reservoirs, from where it was piped to the house by gravity.

Until about 1915, when a hydroelectric scheme was introduced, all the lighting of the house was by candles and oil lamps. One of the original Nash-era chandeliers is still in place and has not been converted to electricity. The water turbine was driven by water carried in large-bore, cast-iron pipes from a weir, forming a man-made lake some distance from the house. The electricity was stored in batteries in a building next to the turbine house. The DC supply was used solely for lighting and for the many bell-pushes throughout the house.

In the eighteenth and nineteenth centuries, the house was heated entirely by open fires. However, partial central heating was installed during Inigo Thomas's expansion work in the early-twentieth century. Radiators were not provided in the bedrooms; instead, they were restricted to the main reception rooms and the first-floor landing. The central-heating boiler in the basement also provided hot water for the bathrooms. The original dressing rooms of the principal bedrooms were converted into bathrooms as part of Inigo Thomas's alterations. It was the introduction of bathrooms that made necessary a piped supply with a sufficient head of water to reach the upper floors of the house and prompted the provision of a piped supply from the other side of the valley. At the same time as water closets were installed in the family bathrooms, two additional ones were provided on the guest-wing corridors, as well as a slop closet for cleaning chamber pots. The drains from the house were channelled into a large, rectangular, covered and lined cess pit that stretched from the north side of the house to the south-west side, from where waste water passed into a soakaway in a field on the south side of the house.

In the kitchen thee was a dumb waiter, and an enclosed kitchen range (installed by W. James and Son of Cardigan in the early-twentieth century), which replaced an earlier Victorian range.

There was a glasshouse in the kitchen garden, heated using water pipes and horse manure. The manure was stored in a large pit outside the glasshouse, and the water pipes were buried in the manure. The heat from the fermenting manure warmed the circulating pipes, which were carried in underfloor troughs into the glasshouse. The troughs were filled with water and covered by lattice-work grilles. The system was capable of producing exactly the right levels of heat and humidity required.

GOLDEN GROVE (GELLI AUR), CARMARTHENSHIRE

(Golden Grove is not currently open to the public)

Fig 97. Golden Grove.

BACKGROUND HISTORY

The Vaughan family first settled in Golden Grove, Carmarthenshire, when John Vaughan built a house on the site in the mid-sixteenth century. In 1729, much of the original house was destroyed by fire. The extensive Golden Grove estate, and what was left of the house, then passed through various branches of the family until it came into the possession of another John Vaughan in 1751. With the help of his son, Richard, during the period 1754–8, he rebuilt the house, but chose not to live there, saying 'I own I am no friend to green walks in Wales, where there is so much rain' (Dyfed County Council, 1982, p.8). When his son, inherited the estate in 1765, it extended to over 50,000 acres. Richard died in 1780 and the house was inherited by his son, John Vaughan, who died without an heir in 1804 and left the estate to his friend, John Campbell.

In 1826, John Campbell's son and heir, John Frederick Campbell (created Earl Cawdor in 1827), demolished the house and began building a new one several hundred yards higher up the slope from the old house. The new house was completed in 1834 and the Cawdor family descendants lived there for the next hundred years, until they moved to Nairn in the 1930s.

TECHNOLOGY

There is little evidence of modern domestic technology in the house built in the 1750s, but a water closet was installed in 1782 and a cold-water plunge bath in 1788. The 1821 inventory of the contents of the house listed a shower bath and bidet in John Vaughan's dressing room, and two pot cupboards and a washstand in the bedroom. In the bedroom over the study, there was a bidet and commode. Similarly, in the 'Castle Room' there was a night table, washstand and bidet. In both the 'Yellow Room' and the 'Green Room', there was a night table and bidet. In fact, bidets were found in three of the four remaining bedrooms and in one other dressing room. The valet's room had a washstand and footbath. Most bedrooms had washstands and there were tin baths in a lumber-room, presumably brought out when required.

In the new house, built in the 1820s and 1830s, there was a top-lit hall, water closets in the main house and privies for the service range. There was a water closet provided for upper servants, but access to it was from outside the house. The extensive service range included a kitchen, scullery, pantry, wet and dry laundries, dairy, brew house, bake house, and numerous rooms for luggage, coal, knives and shoes, etc.

On the Chamber Floor there were two water closets, one leading off the master bedroom and one serving the other bedrooms. An ingeniously contrived rainwater system for flushing the water closets (referred to in the text) was built into the tower.

A limited electricity supply was provided in the 1890s, initially driven by a steam engine, but that was replaced by a new, much more extensive system in 1905, consisting of a gas engine, new batteries, a new dynamo, a gas producer and rewiring, at a total cost of £638 (Cawdor Archives 2/234, Carmarthenshire Archives Service). Including the service range and stables, there were 189 light fittings and eight 'plug connections' for table lamps, etc. Only eight of the eleven bedrooms were lit by electricity.

In the 1908 inventory, foot baths, commodes, hip baths and bidets are still listed (Cawdor Archives, 2/180, Carmarthenshire Archives Service), suggesting that, even by that date, there was little in the way of bathroom facilities for family and guests.

LLANERCHAERON, CEREDIGION

(Llanerchaeron is a National Trust property.)

Fig 98. Llanerchaeron.

BACKGROUND HISTORY

Though it incorporated an earlier seventeenth-century building, Llanerchaeron is primarily an example of a late-eighteenth century Welsh manor house. The Llanerchaeron estate was the property of the Lewis family. When John Lewis died in 1789, the estate passed to his son, William, who had married Corbetta Williama Powell, the daughter of Dr Powell of Nanteos in 1786.

William and Corbetta set about modernising the old house, employing the architect John Nash to undertake the work, which was completed in the 1790s. William Lewis was a JP and High Sheriff of Cardiganshire. William and Corbetta had a son and daughter, and on the death of William in 1828, the son, John, inherited the house and estate. He married Mary Ashby Mettam in 1841, but they had no children. John predeceased his wife in 1855 and on her death in 1917, the estate passed to her great nephew, Thomas Powell Lewes, on whose death in 1940, it passed to his son, John Powell Ponsonby Lewis. In 1989 the house was left to the National Trust.

TECHNOLOGY

When John Lewis inherited the house in 1828, domestic technology had not advanced appreciably from the 1790s and there was therefore little need to make changes. On his death, his widow (who was merely a tenant for life) was restricted as to what changes she could make, because any alterations needed to be approved by the trustees of her husband's will. She also grew set in her ways and chose not to make significant changes. When the estate passed to Thomas Powell Lewes in 1917, he began introducing modern domestic technology into the house. Within two years, he had installed electric lighting and servants bells. The dynamo was driven by a waterwheel from the Eagle Foundry, Aberystwyth, which was originally installed in 1852, to drive the saw mill. The system provided electric lighting to the ground floor and to one or two of the main bedrooms (Lloyd Evans, 2012, p.33). Thomas Lewes also installed the first bathroom at Llanerchaeron, by carving it out of the backstairs landing and what had formerly been a servant's bedroom. Access to the bathroom from the family bedrooms was via a door leading from the landing onto the backstairs. Until the bathroom was installed, the whole household relied on chamber pots, hip baths and washbowls for sanitation, washing and bathing.

Central heating was not included in the modernisation programme initiated by Thomas Lewes, so Llanerchaeron was heated solely by open fires during its entire history.

Separate privy leats were provided for indoor and outdoor servants. The outdoor servants had a three-seater privy-leat toilet and the indoor servants had a two-seater, built close to the service range.

The walled kitchen gardens date from the late eighteenth century and, certainly by the early-nineteenth century, contained heated glass houses and hot walls. Further heated glass houses were added in the mid-nineteenth century.

MIDDLETON HALL. CARMARTHENSHIRE

(The house was destroyed by fire in 1931, but the grounds
now form the National Botanic Garden of Wales.)

Fig 99. Middleton Hall.

BACKGROUND HISTORY

The original Middleton Hall was built in the seventeenth century for
Henry Middleton, who was High Sheriff of Carmarthenshire in 1644. His
son, Christopher, and grandson, Richard, were also High Sheriffs of the
county, in 1668 and 1701 respectively. Richard Middleton died in 1733 and
the house and estate passed to his son, Henry. When he died, the estate
passed to his sister, Elizabeth, who married Thomas Gwyn of Gwempa.
Thomas and Elizabeth died in 1752 and 1756 respectively, and their eldest
son, Richard, inherited the estate. He was High Sheriff in 1761. However,
by 1767 he had amassed debts of £10,000 and spent several years in the
King's bench prison. His son, Francis, increased the mortgages on the
house, until by 1776 the total debts had reached almost £40,000 and he was
forced to sell the estate, which was ulitimately bought by William Paxton
(1744-1824) in 1789. Paxton had made his fortune in India and was not
reliant on income from land to fund his building projects and lifestyle.

Between 1793 and 1795, a totally new hall was built, designed by Samuel Pepys Cockerell, and the old hall became the home farm. The new house was generally acknowledged to be grand, elegant and magnificent (Jones, 2006, p. 132). Paxton was Mayor of Carmarthen in 1802, was knighted in 1803 and was briefly the MP for Carmarthen in 1806.

On Paxton's death in 1824 the estate was sold to Edward Adams, who had made his wealth in Jamaica. Adams was High Sheriff for Carmarthenshire in 1831 and MP for Carmarthenshire in 1833. On his death the house passed to his son, who changed his name to Abadam. The house remained in the Abadam family until it was sold in 1919, but it was then left unoccupied until it was destroyed by fire in 1931.

TECHNOLOGY

When the house was sold in 1824, there were water closets in the dressing room, the lobby and possibly one serving the principal guest bedroom. There were housemaids' closets and a number of storage cisterns fed by reservoirs and a spring on the hills above the house. There was an extensive service range consisting of a kitchen, scullery, wet and dry laundries, dairy, brew house, bake house, as well as ample servants' accommodation. Water was piped to a number of the key rooms in the service range, and there was also an eighteenth-century icehouse, a three-acre, double-walled garden (also dating from the eighteenth century) and a 36-foot long conservatory. Within the walled garden, there was a glasshouse heated by underfloor heating. Paxton also built a bathhouse for the private use of the family and their guests.

NANTEOS, CEREDIGION

(Nanteos is now a country-house hotel.)

Fig 100. Nanteos.

BACKGROUND HISTORY

There is evidence of a house at Nanteos from at least the seventeenth century, when it was lived in by William and Anne Powell, who had lead and silver mining interests. In the early 1720s, their eldest son, Thomas, married Mary Frederick, the daughter of a wealthy London businessman. She brought great wealth to the marriage and, following the death of his father in 1739, Thomas and Mary spent much of it rebuilding Nanteos. Thomas Powell was MP for Cardigan (1725–1727) and for Cardiganshire (1741–1747) (Morgan, 2001, pp.25-6).

The new house was intended to reflect their wealth, status and ambitions. Unfortunately for Thomas, it was not fully completed until five years after his death in 1752. The house and estate then passed to his younger brother, the Rev. Doctor William Powell (1705-80), and when he died to his son, Thomas (1745-97), by which time the estate measured a total of 30,000 acres.

Thomas Powell married Eleanor Corbett, with whom he had four children. The eldest, William Edward Powell (1788-1854), was only nine-years-old when he inherited the estate, but by then it was already £20,000 in debt. William Edward Powell served as Lord Lieutenant of the County, as Sheriff (1810) and as MP for Cardiganshire (from 1816 until his death).

Although heavily in debt, he and his mother lived a lavish lifestyle. He bought a commission in the Royal Cardiganshire Regiment and kept racehorses at Newmarket. His mother spent much of her time in the social whirl of London, Bath and Dublin, but had to flee to France in 1812 to escape her creditors (Jones, 2004, p.201).

In 1810, William married Laura Edwina Phelp, the eldest daughter of Col. James Phelp, a deputy Lieutenant of Leicestershire, a JP and the squire of Coston House, Glamorganshire. Unfortunately, while William was away – either in Newmarket or commanding his regiment in Ireland – the estate was badly managed.

He returned to Nanteos in 1815, but even with his wife's dowry of £3,000 they became increasingly debt-ridden – due partly to the fact that he attempted to raise his status in the county by serving as Lord Lieutenant and MP for Cardiganshire. Both posts were a serious drain on the estate's finances because they involved considerable expense, not least in terms of providing hospitality and largesse.

William Powell clearly preferred London to west Wales. So, while Laura remained in Nanteos, he spent much of his time in the capital, where he kept a mistress and got himself into ever-greater debt. On Laura's death in 1822, William returned to Nanteos and, even with growing debts, made further improvements to the house. He built an impressive new stable block in the 1830s and an icehouse in 1831. He added an east wing to the house in 1841, additional service range provision in 1846, and a portico and dining room in 1848 (Parkinson in Morgan, 2001, p.170; Palmer in Morgan, pp.206-7). The money for these improvements was raised largely by selling off land and by leasing land he owned in Aberystwyth for development.

On William's death in 1854, his eldest son, William Thomas Powell (1815-78), inherited the estate and attempted to bring some order to the estate finances.

Between 1868 and 1873, he raised £80,000 by selling off land, but in the process reduced the estate to 21,000 acres. (Lloyd, et al, 2006, pp.547-8). His main addition to the house was the building of a billiard room in the 1860s.

On his death in 1878, he was succeeded by his son, George (1842-84), a poet and friend of Byron, Swinburne, Longfellow and Wagner (Jones, 2004, p.201). He married but died childless, and the estate passed to his cousin, William Beauclerk Powell (1834-1911). William, and later his son, Edward, continued to sell off land, until the size of the estate was reduced to 4,000 acres. Edward married the daughter of Sir Pryse Pryse of Gogerddan, but their only son, William, was killed in the First World War. With the death of Edward Powell in 1930, the Powell's connection with Nanteos finally came to an end.

TECHNOLOGY

The original kitchen garden had walls erected between around 1812 and 1817, and it ultimately contained a melon house, a heated vinery and a glasshouse. There was also a flower garden with a heated orchid house (Palmer in Morgan, 2001, p.214). In the nineteenth century, a rotating summer house was built, which was engineered so that it could be turned into, or out of, the sun.

There was an extensive service range, with some outlying buildings, all built loosely around a service court yard. The service range included a kitchen, servants' hall, dairy, wet and dry laundries, a bakery and a brew house. By the end of the nineteenth century, the kitchen had a closed kitchen range, two charcoal ranges and a heated warming cabinet.

There was total reliance on coal and log fires at Nanteos; indeed, central heating was only introduced after the Second World War. And until 1914, when electric lighting was introduced, the house was lit entirely by candles and oil lamps.

The 1914 electricity supply lighting was provided by a small petrol engine and DC dynamo. Lighting was installed throughout the house and service range. In total, eighty-two light fittings were provided, several of which were table lamps supplied from wall sockets. In addition, there were two power points, one in the engine house and one in the battery house.

Water was supplied from a stream high above the house, which fed into a pond and then into an underground storage tank set into the hillside. It was piped from there to the house, the stable block and the service range.

The underground storage tank had a sufficient head of water to reach the upper floors of the house when water closets were installed in the nineteenth century. Water from the storage tank was also piped to a slate-cistern at the rear of the service range. This ran continuously and the overflow from the cistern passed into the main drain running beneath the cellar in the house. All the rainwater and liquid waste from the house discharged into this drain, which led to a stream some distance away from the house.

It is unclear when water closets were installed at Nanteos, but it was probably during the improvements undertaken in the 1830s and 1840s. When they were installed, they were provided for both family and servants. There was a water closet on the first floor that served the family and guests, and one on the second floor that served the nursery. There were outdoor water closets on the ground floor for kitchen staff, which probably replaced earlier privy-leat toilets, and two indoor water closets near the butler's pantry for use by the upper servants.

There were three privy-leat toilets near the walled garden. Two were separate but adjacent to each other, and were for use by the gardeners. The third, some distance from these, is believed to have been solely for the use of Captain Powell.

There was no attempt to provide hot and cold piped water supplies to bathrooms at Nanteos. The family and their guests made use of wash basins and hip baths, either in their bedrooms or their dressing rooms.

There was a bell board in the corridor of the service range, linked to all the key locations in the house (seventeen in total). They were operated using cranked levers and a wire and pulley system.

Near the service range, there was a short stretch of railway. This took coal and logs from the main delivery point (near the tradesmen's entrance) to the coal and log store in the service range courtyard. A truck would be loaded with coal at the main delivery point and then pushed at speed along the track until it hit a buffer, which upended the coal truck and emptied the contents into the yard below.

Newton House, Carmarthenshire

(Newton house is owned by the National Trust.)

Fig 101. Newton House.

Background history

Newton House is an example of a country house that evolved over several centuries, from 1660 when the original house was built to 1856–7 when it was remodelled, and then to the close of the nineteenth century when further improvements were made. Although the present house was built for the fourth Baron Dynevor during the rebuilding boom of the nineteenth century, it was essentialy an encasing of the previous seventeenth-century house, which may itself have been built on the site of an even earlier fifteenth century house.

In 1756, the owner of Newton House, George Rice (MP for Carmarthenshire 1754-1779), married Cecil Talbot of the wealthy Talbot family. Her father, William Talbot, was made Baron Dynevor in 1780. When he died without a male heir, the title passed to Cecil and then to her son, George Talbot Rice. As well as a title, Cecil brought great wealth to the Rice family, and although she and her successors spent little time at Newton House, a significant amount of her wealth was invested in the house and estate. Her son, George Talbot Rice, became an MP in 1790. He married Francis Townshend in 1794, and they had three sons and six daughters – only one of the sons survived, however. When George Talbot Rice died in 1852, he was succeeded by his sole surviving son (also called George) and it was he who was largely responsible for the Newton House of today. That remodelling work took place largely between 1856 and 1857, and was certainly completed by 1859. George had married Francis Fitzroy in 1824 and though they had five daughters, there was no male heir. On his death in 1869, therefore, his extensive landholdings of 30,000 acres were divided up, with the title and the Dinefwr estate passing to his cousin Francis William Rice. Francis spent little time at Dinefwr and when he died in 1878, his son, Arthur, inherited the estate, but soon began selling parts of it off, with sales in 1882, 1886 and 1895. His son, Walter, continued the sale of land in 1919 and 1920 (Morgan, 2014).

TECHNOLOGY

Newton House was built on a flood plain and so could not rely on gravity to supply water to the house. Instead, water for cooking, cleaning, bathing and washing was pumped by a waterwheel from a well to the service range.

During the remodelling of Newton house in the 1850s, a new pump house was built and a new water wheel installed. The pump house was at the lower end of an ornamental lake and part of the outflow from the lake drove the waterwheel, which was linked to a pump. Water was pumped to storage tanks on the hillside and then carried by gravity to the service range.

Following a fire in 1896, fire hydrants and hoses were installed in and around the house. The hydrants were supplied with water from separate storage tanks on the hillside above the house. In 1920, the waterwheel was supplemented by a diesel engine.

Spring water was fed into a tank with 2,500-gallon capacity and a ram pump (installed in 1900) pumped it to another tank, from where it was carried by gravity to the first floor of the brew house and then on to the main house for drinking water.

Electricity was installed in 1928, using an acetylene gas producer, a gas engine and an AC generator. It provided electric lighting and some mechanical equipment in the dairy.

A billiard room and smoking room were added in 1896, along with three water closets for the gentlemen. Between 1898 and 1911 bathrooms and water closets for the family were installed in the four turret towers, and a bathroom, urinals and water closet were provided in the basement for the servants.

Wastewater from the house and service range was carried by drains to a soakaway some distance from the house. During the Second World War, when the army created a military hospital in the grounds, that form of sewage disposal was upgraded, with the army installing percolating filter beds.

Central heating was not introduced into the house while it was a family home; all the heating was by coal fires.

In the grounds, there is a late-eighteenth or early-nineteenth century icehouse. There was also a walled kitchen garden some distance from the house, with vinery, hot walls and heated glass houses.

STACKPOLE COURT, PEMBROKESHIRE.

(Stackpole Court was demolished in 1963; the National
Trust now own the parkland and gardens.)

Fig 102. Stackpole Court.

BACKGROUND HISTORY

Sir Alexander Campbell of Cawdor Castle in Scotland acquired the estate
on the death of his wife, Elizabeth Lort, in 1714. Sir Alexander's son, John
Campbell, married Mary, the eldest daughter and co-heiress of Lewis Pryse
of Gogerddan, and together they began to transform the existing house,
gardens and estate, with the bulk of the rebuilding work taking place in
the 1730s. John Campbell died in 1777 and because his eldest son had
predeceased him, the house and estate passed to his younger son, John. The
younger John Campbell was created the first Lord Cawdor in 1796. When
he died in 1821, he was succeeded by his son, John Frederick Vaughan
Campbell (1790-1860), who was made Earl of Cawdor in 1827. During the
1820s and 1830s, he enlarged the house and made significant improvements

156

to it. His son, Frederick Archibald Vaughan (1847-1911), was Lord Lieutenant of Pembrokeshire (1896–1911) and MP for Carmarthenshire (1874–1885). By 1873, the family owned 51,538 acres in Carmarthenshire, Pembrokeshire and Cardiganshire, with an estimated annual rental of £35,043. Their principal residence remained Stackpole Court until the beginning of the twentieth century, when they made Cawdor Castle in Scotland their main home. John Duncan Vaughan (1900–1970), the fifth Earl Cawdor, spent most of his time in Scotland and sold the contents of Stackpole Court in 1962. The house was demolished the following year.

TECHNOLOGY

By 1782, the lakes had been created, along with pleasure gardens, a walled garden and a new deer park (in addition to an earlier one).

In 1839, the principal bedroom had two dressing rooms, one of which contained a water closet. Next to this suite of rooms was a bathroom, with beneath it a boiler to provide the necessary hot water. Access to the bathroom was, however, from the corridor rather than the bedroom. A suite of bedrooms for female guests contained a private lobby and water closet, and similarly the male guest wing had a corridor with access to a water closet. There was also a water closet in the servants' sleeping quarters, and a housemaids' closet with a slop sink.

The service range included a kitchen, scullery, washhouse, bake house and brew house. Outside the service range there was a large coal yard containing a number of privy middens for use by the servants.

In the grounds, there was a walled kitchen garden, glasshouses and an icehouse. A gas works was built on the estate in the 1860s, presumably to provide gas lighting for the house, service range and stables (Lloyd, 2004, pp.462-3).

STRADEY AND STRADEY CASTLE, LLANELLI

(Stradey Castle is in private ownership, but open
to the public on request and for functions.)

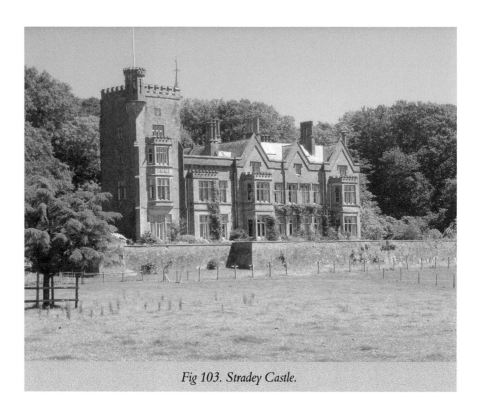

Fig 103. Stradey Castle.

BACKGROUND HISTORY

In 1673, Sir Henry Vaughan of Derwydd, the owner of the Stradey estate, granted the house and estate in perpetuity to Edward Mansel, the grandson of John Mansel, who had earlier married into the Vaughan family. Edward Mansel died in 1798 without leaving a will, and the estate passed to his sister, Mary Anne. She died in 1808 without an heir, and she bequeathed the house and estate to Thomas Lewis, the family solicitor, who had managed the estate on her behalf following the death of her husband in 1806. Between 1820 and his death in 1829, Thomas Lewis completed extensive work on the house, increasing its size from sixteen to thirty-three rooms.

Thomas Lewis was succeeded by his son, David Lewis, who decided in the 1840s to relocate the house to its present position on higher ground, so as to gain a better view of the sea and parkland. The building of Stradey Castle was completed between 1848 and 1855. On the death of David Lewis in 1872, the house passed to his son, Charles William Mansel Lewis, who enlarged the house still further between 1873 and 1875, with the addition of the north-west wing and the distinctive tower.

TECHNOLOGY

The eighteenth-century house of Stradey boasted little in the way of modern technology. It was lit by candles and oil lamps, heated by open fires, and the family made use of traditional washing, bathing and sanitary arrangements. However, in the 1820s, a water closet was installed, along with an associated borehole, pump and cistern.

The new house reflected the changing technology and desires of the nineteenth century. It was one of the first houses in Wales to have electric lighting, and by the end of the century had both central heating and indoor plumbing.

There was a walled kitchen garden and heated peach house.

Appendix B

Servant numbers based on census records

Scolton Manor	1881	1891	1901	1911
Cook	1	1	1	1
Parlour Maid	1		1	1
Housemaid	1	1	1	1
Nurse	1	1		
Kitchen Maid	1	1		1
Dairymaid	1	1	1	
Under Dairymaid	1			
Coachman			1	
Stable boy/groom	1	1	1	1
Total	8	6	6	5

Table 1: Scolton Manor

Cilwendeg	1851	1861	1871	1901
Butler	1	1	1	
Cook	1	1	1	1
Lady's maid	1	1	1	
Housemaid	3	1	1	3
Footman	1	1	1	
Kitchen maid	1	1	1	
Laundry maid	1			
Dairy maid	1	2	2	1
Coachman	1	1	1	1
Groom		1	1	2
Postboy		1	1	
Total	**11**	**11**	**11**	**8**

Table 2: Cilwendeg

Llanerchaeron	1861	1871
Butler	1	1
Housekeeper	1	
Cook		1
Lady's maid	1	1
Housemaid	2	2
Footman		1
Laundry maid	1	1
Dairy maid	1	1
Coachman	1	
Total	**8**	**8**

Table 3: Llanerchaeron

Bronwydd	1851	1861	1871	1881	1911
Butler	1	1	1		1
Housekeeper	1			1	
Tutor/governess			1		
Cook	1		1	1	1
Lady's maid	1	1		1	2
Valet				1	
Housemaid	1	2	2	2	2
Footman	1		1		1
Nurse	1			1	1
Nursery maid	1				
Kitchen maid	1	1	1	1	1
Dairy maid	2		2	1	
Laundry maid			1	1	
Coachman	1		1		
Chauffeur					1
Groom	1		1	1	1
Pantry boy	1				
Total	**14**	**5**	**12**	**11**	**11**

Table 4: Bronwydd
Note: It is likely that there was some extraneous and specific reason for the drastic drop in servant number in 1861.

Nanteos	1871	1881	1891	1901
Butler		1	1	1
Housekeeper	1	1		
Cook			1	1
Under cook	2		2	2
Housemaid		2	1	1
Nurse	1			1
Kitchen maid	1			
Coachman				1
Groom				1
Total	**5**	**4**	**5**	**8**

Table 5: Nanteos
Note: In 1911, the specific occupations were not given in the census return for Nanteos, but there were four female and two male servants listed.

Bibliography

- Ashenburg, K. (2008) *Clean: An Unsanitised History of Washing*, Profile Books, London.
- Aslet, C. (1982) *The Last Country Houses* Yale University Press, New Haven.
- Baker-Jones, L. (1999) *Princelings Privilege and Power: The Tivyside Gentry in their Community*, Gomer Press, Llandysul.
- Baker-Jones, L. (2005) *The Wolf and the Boar: The Lloyds of Bronwydd Cardiganshire: Lords Marcher of Cemais*, Quatrefoil Books, Llandysul.
- Baker-Jones, L. (Ed), (2001), *The Glaspant Diary 1896: A Chronicle of Carmarthenshire Country Life*, Carmarthenshire County Council, Carmarthen.
- Barnwell, P.S. and Palmer, M. (eds) (2012) *Country House Technology*, Shaun Tyas, Donington.
- Bennett Morgan, P. (1984) *Bronwydd and Sir Thomas Lloyd* Welsh Journals on Line (National Library of Wales) (pp.378-401)
- Briggs, R.A. (1911) *The Essentials of a Country House*, Batsford, London.
- Campbell, S. (2005) *A History of Kitchen Gardening*, Francis Lincoln, London.
- Christie, C. (2000) *The British Country House in the Eighteenth Century*, Manchester University Press, Manchester.
- Dyfed County Council. (1982) *Gelli Aur Country Park,* Estate Printers, Treforest.
- Evans, S. (2011) *Life Below Stairs in the Victorian & Edwardian Country House National* Trust, London.
- Eveleigh, D.J. (2006), *Bogs, Baths & Basins: The Story of Domestic Sanitation*, Sutton, Stroud.
- Farrer, J. (1865) *Recollections of Seventy Years by Mrs John Farrar*, Tickler and Fields, Boston.

- Franklin, J. (1981), *The Gentleman's Country House and its Plan, 1835-1914*, Routledge Kegan & Paul, London.
- Fenton, R. (1810) [2011] *A Historical Tour Through Pembrokeshire*, Rare Books, Memphis.
- Gerard, J. (1994) *Country House Life: Family and Servants 1815-1914*, Blackwell, Oxford.
- Gerhard, W.P. (1914) [2004] *The Sanitation, Water Supply and Sewage Disposal of Country Houses*, Fredonia Books, Amsterdam.
- Girouard, M. (1984), *Life in the English Country House*, Yale University Press, New Haven.
- Girouard, M. (1985) *The Victorian Country House*, Yale University Press, New Haven.
- Hardyment, C. (1997*), Behind the Scenes: Domestic Arrangements in Historic House*s. National Trust Enterprises, London.
- Horn, P. (1990), *The Rise and Fall of the Victorian Servant*, Sutton, Stroud.
- Horn, P. (2013) *Country House Society: The private lives of England's upper class after the First World War* Amberly Publishing, Stroud.
- Howell, D.W. (1986), *Patriarchs & Parasites: The Gentry of South-West Wales in the Eighteenth Century*, Cardiff University Press, Cardiff.
- Joel, J. (2014) *Nanteos Walled Garden*
- Jones, F, (1975) Journal of a Young Lady of Fashion, *The Carmarthenshire Historian*, Vol, XII, Dyfed Rural Council, Carmarthen.
- Jones, F. (2001) *Historic Pembrokeshire Homes and Their Families,* Brawdy Books, Newport.
- Jones, F. (2006) *Historic Carmarthenshire Homes and Their Families* Brawdy Books, Pembrokeshire.
- Kerr, R. (1864) [2012] *The Gentleman's House or, How to Plan English Residences, from the Parsonage to the Palace,* Cambridge University Press, New York.
- Lloyd, T, Orbach, J, Scourfield, R. (2004) *The Buildings of Wales: Pembrokeshire*, Yale University Press, London.
- Lloyd, T. Orbach, J, Scourfield, R. (2005) *The Buildings of Wales: Carmarthenshire and Ceredigion*, Yale University Press, London.
- Lloyd Evans, M. (2012) *Llanerchaeron: A Tale of 10 Generations 1634-1989,* Y Lolfa, Talybont.
- Mingay, G.E. (1976) *The Gentry: The Rise and Fall of a Ruling Class*, Longman, London.

- Morgan, G. (ed) (2001) *Nanteos: A Welsh House and its Families* Gomer Press, Llandysul.
- Morgan, G. (2014) *Dinefwr: A Phoenix in Wales*, Gomer Press, Llandysul.
- Morris, M.G.R. (ed) (1998) *Romilly's Visits to Wales 1827-1854*, Gomer, Llandysul.
- Orbach, J. (1995) *Cilwendeg, Boncath: Three Hundred Years of a House and Forty Years of the Residential Home 1955-95*, Dyfed County Council, Carmarthen.
- Palmer C, David P, and Laidlow R, (2004) *Historic Parks and Gardens in Ceredigion*, WHGT, Llandeilo.
- Paterson, M. (2012) *Private Life in Britain's Stately Homes: Masters and Servants in the Golden Age*, Constable and Robinson, London.
- Phillips, B. (1997) *Peterwell: The History of a Mansion and its Infamous Squire,* Cymdeitha Lyfrau Ceredigion Gyf, Aberystwyth.
- Reid, G. (1901) *Practical Sanitation: A handbook for Sanitary Inspectors and others interested in Sanitation.* Charles Griffin, London.
- Roberts, B, (1997) *The Quest for Comfort,* IMI Waterheating.
- Roberts, B, (2001) *The Magic of Hot Water,* Andrews Water Heaters.
- Rolf, V. (2011) *Bathing House and Plunge Pools*, Shire Publications, Oxford.
- Sambrook, P. (1996) *Country House Brewing in England 1500-1900*, Hambledon Press, London.
- Sambrook, P. (1999) *The Country House Servant* Sutton Publishing, Stroud.
- Sambrook, A.P. and Brears, P. (1997) *The Country House Kitchen 1650-1900*, Sutton Publishing, Stroud
- Sambrook, P. (2009) *Keeping Their Place: Domestic Service in the Country House,* The History Press, Stroud.
- Stevenson, J.J. (1880) *House Architecture Vol II*, Macmillan, London.
- Suggett, R. (1995) *John Nash: Architect in Wales*, National Library of Wales, Aberystwyth.
- Taine, H. (1885) *Notes on England*, Henry Holt and Co, New York
- Thompson, F.M.L. (1963) *English Landed Society in the Nineteenth Century,* Routledge & Kegan Paul, London.
- Vaughan, H.M. (1926) [1988] *The South Wales Squires*, Golden Grove, Carmarthen.

- Waterson, M. (1993) *The Servants' Hall: A Domestic History of Erddig*, The National Trust, London.
- Weaver, L. (ed) (1912) [2005] *The House and Its Equipment*, Newnes, London.
- Woods, M, and Warren, A. (1990) *Glass Houses: A History of Greenhouses, Orangeries and Conservatories*, Aurum Press, Lonndon.

List of Illustrations

- Fig 29. The Llandeilo Butter and Cheese Factory, (Courtesy of Carmarthen Museum Service).
- Fig 30. The servants' bells at Alltyrodyn.
- Fig 31. The electric bell board at Ffynone.
- Fig 32. A schematic illustration of a hand-pump.
- Fig 33. A kitchen maid drawing water using a double-acting hand pump in the service-range courtyard at Alltyferin, (Courtesy of Carmarthen Museum Service).
- Fig 34. The weir at Ffynone.
- Fig 35. An underground, spring-water storage reservoir serving Ffynone, (Photograph courtesy of Howard Jenkins).
- Fig 36. A washstand with chamber pot, washbowl and ewer.
- Fig 37. A hip bath, Penrhyn Castle, Gwynedd (© National Trust / Kane Thomas & Clare Turgoose).
- Fig 38. A portable shower bath, (© National Trust/David Midgelow).
- Fig 39. The early-twentieth century bathroom at Llanerchaeron.
- Fig 40. The water wheel in the pump house at Newton House.
- Fig 42. The diesel Engine in the pump house at Newton House.
- Fig 43. The ram pump in the pump house at Newton House.
- Fig 44. A schematic illustration of a ram pump.
- Fig 45. A schematic illustration of a 'direct' hot-water system.
- Fig 46. The servants' bathroom at Newton House.
- Fig 47. A close stool, (©National Trust Images/Susanne Gronnow).
- Fig 48. A slop Pail at Llanerchaeron.
- Fig 49. The improved, Bramah-type valve closet.
- Fig 50. An example of a pan closet.
- Fig 51. A schematic illustration of the rainwater system at Golden Grove.
- Fig 52. The Stradey Castle valve closet in the entrance-hall cloakroom (photograph courtesy of Howard Jenkins).
- Fig 53. Water closet serving one of the guest wings at Ffynone (photograph courtesy of Howard Jenkins).
- Fig 54. One of the servants' bedrooms at Llanerchaeron.
- Fig 55. An exterior view of the privy leat at Alltyrodyn.
- Fig 56. The interior of one of the privy leats at Llanerchaeron.
- Fig 57. The leat serving one of the privies at Nanteos.
- Fig 58. An advertisement for a wash-down water closet, complete with waste-water preventing cistern, c.1881.
- Fig 59. A schematic illustration of a siphonic flushing cistern and ball valve.
- Fig 60. The percolating filter bed at Falcondale.
- Fig 61. The inner vestibule and double fanlights at Alltyrodyn.
- Fig 62. One of the principal fireplaces at Stradey Castle (photograph courtesy of Howard Jenkins).
- Fig 63. Fire dogs (© National Trust).
- Fig 64. Coal grate (© National Trust/Sue James).
- Fig 65. Stradey Castle (photograph courtesy of Howard Jenkins).
- Fig 66. Top-lit landing at Llanerchaeron.
- Fig 67. Bronwydd (Courtesy of St Fagans National History Museum).

- Fig 68. A chandelier at Ffynone (photograph courtesy of Howard Jenkins).
- Fig 69. An Argand lamp showing the circular wick arrangement and the glass chimney.
- Fig 70. An Argand oil lamp showing the oil reservoir raised above the wick. (© National Trust/Bryan Rutledge).
- Fig 71. A typical coal-gas installation of about 1845 suitable for use in country houses.
- Fig 72. An acetylene gas plant (from the Tom Mathias Collection, Courtesy of Pembrokeshire Museum Service).
- Fig 73. Stradey Castle – the inlet from the holding tank to the water turbine.
- Fig 74. The Stradey Castle water turbine.
- Fig 75. The belt-drive wheel at Stradey Castle.
- Fig 76. The water wheel and line-shafting at Llanerchaeron.
- Fig 77. The Clynfyw hydroelectric installation.
- Fig 78. The Clynfyw millpond and boating lake.
- Fig 79. Clynfyw Servants 1906 (From the Tom Mathias Collection, courtesy of Pembrokeshire Museum Service).
- Fig 80. One of the dipping ponds at Llanerchaeron.
- Fig 81. A second dipping pond at Llanerchaeron.
- Fig 82. Heating pipes in a greenhouse at Llanerchaeron.
- Fig 83. The Orangery at Margam Park.
- Fig 84. The restored pineapple house at Scolton Manor (courtesy of Pembrokeshire Museum Service).
- Fig 85. The tiled Floor and Grill in the Conservatory at Cilwendeg.
- Fig 86. A schematic illustration of an icehouse.
- Fig 87. The entrance passage in the ice house at Middleton Hall.
- Fig 88. The door-rebate in the entrance passage to Middleton Hall icehouse.
- Fig 89. The entrance passage to the Newton House icehouse.
- Fig 90. The icehouse at Newton House.
- Fig. 92. Aberglasney (Courtesy of Carmarthen Museum Service).
- Fig 93. Alltyrodyn Mansion
- Fig 94. Bronwydd (Courtesy of St Fagans National History Museum).
- Fig 95. Cilwendeg.
- Fig 96. Ffynone (Photograph courtesy of Howard Jenkins).
- Fig 97. Golden Grove (Courtesy of Carmarthen Museum Service).
- Fig 98. Llanerchaeron.
- Fig 99. Middleton Hall (Courtesy of the National Botanic Garden of Wales, reproduced with the kind permission of the Grant family).
- Fig 100. Nanteos.
- Fig 101. Newton House.
- Fig 102. Stackpole Court (Courtesy of Carmarthen Museum Service).
- Fig 103. Stradey Castle.

INDEX